Tiny Footprints

This book is dedicated to the 12 million babies worldwide who arrive too early every single year. Many of these tiny babies fight against such difficulties and adversities just to survive. This book is also dedicated to the memory of the 1 million babies worldwide who die each year as a result of complications following their premature birth.

There is no foot so small that it cannot leave an imprint on our lives.

ISBN: 978-1-908559-02-9

Printed and bound in Ireland by eprint limited, www.eprint.ie

Editorial team:

Allison Fegan Molloy
Liz Lewis
Sarah Murphy
Tara Mackin

Copy-editor: Elizabeth Hudson, at the Little Red Pen

Contents

Contributors

Eighty parents submitted either their own written account of their experience of having a premature baby or a verbal account to one of the editors who subsequently wrote it down verbatim. Each of the parents also selected the photographs to accompany their experience.

The editorial team, from the charity Irish Premature Babies, are deeply appreciative to each family who has permitted us to share their deeply personal and often traumatic account of how having a premature baby has affected their family. Each story resonates with such honesty, openness and love that it was the editorial team's privilege to work on the collaboration for the book.

Acknowledgements

A special thanks to all the parents who have submitted their story. For many people it has been difficult and painful to write their account of having a premature baby. We are extremely grateful to each of you. We want to thank the members of the book team for the months of hard work, diligence and commitment and for their sense of humour, which kept us all going. When you have a job, children, hospital commitments, etc., it's hard to find the time to slot in your voluntary work. We know each of you have given up so much of your free time over the past few months.

It's imperative that we thank all our husbands, Alan, Ken, Keith and Scott for taking over the parental duties at home. We would like to thank the other members of the charity for their support and encouragement and a special thanks to Mandy Daly who we got to read and check each story. Thanks to Elizabeth Hudson for volunteering her time to help and guide us in editing this book. We are enormously grateful.

We would also like to thank Centering Corporation, Nebraska, for granting us permission to use the poem 'Little Footprints' on behalf of Dorothy Ferguson.

Special thanks to Clara and Eugene Ryan, parents of baby Christopher Edward Ryan, for allowing us to take a photograph of their beautiful son for the cover. Thanks to the Coombe Women and Infants University Hospital and Ms. Barbara Whelan for their help. Thanks to the photographer Ger Dunne for taking the photograph, and special thanks to Joan Carty for designing the cover.

Foreword

The seeds for this book were planted with an off-the-cuff comment from a parent on a social-networking page. The concept just gained momentum as we started to talk to families who had amazing, tragic and inspiring stories to tell. These families and their babies became the impetus and motivation behind this book. As you read the stories and marvel at the photographs, we hope the source of our inspiration will become apparent.

We hope that a book like this will also help create awareness of prematurity, not just in Ireland but anywhere it is read. We fully understand that unless you have had a premature baby it can be very difficult to comprehend what it would be like. We hope that this book will give the community at large an insight into what families of premature babies often endure. When you have a healthy term baby, life revolves around feeding, changing and catching the odd hour of sleep. When you have a premature baby, your life revolves around the hospital, dealing with medical and often life-threatening conditions that you never believed a tiny innocent little baby would be subjected to. For the family there is insurmountable stress, exhaustion, fear, isolation and helplessness. Despite the Trojan work of the neonatal staff, there are, sadly, many families who also experience the tragic and heartbreaking loss of their little baby. Even when a baby is discharged from the neonatal unit, parents often have to contend with juggling work and home responsibilities alongside numerous therapies, hospital appointments and long-term complications. This is not the life you envisaged when you become pregnant, but it is the reality for so many parents. In Ireland, there are just over 4,500 babies born premature each year. One in 14 families will have a baby in a neonatal intensive care unit or special care baby unit.

When you have a premature baby, many parents often feel isolated and alone. Premature babies undoubtedly come with their own unique concerns both while in hospital and when they are discharged home. Premature babies can be delayed in reaching developmental milestones, such as talking and walking, and have long-term complications. Unless you know other people or family who have had premature babies, it can be very difficult to express your worries and feel that you are being understood. We hope that parents will find solace in this book amongst fellow parents who really know and understand their situation. The experiences described within the book are from parents living in Ireland, but parents throughout the world can relate to and empathise with the roller-coaster ride that is having a premature baby.

We hope that this book will highlight the amazing stories of inner strength, determination and fortitude that many of these babies possess. These tiny babies, who fight against and recover from numerous conditions and infections, are truly inspiring and absolutely amazing. These are stories that should be told, and our charity is privileged to be able to share with you numerous captivating stories written by the parents of each much-loved baby.

The three Dublin neonatal intensive care units in the maternity hospitals will receive some of the smallest and sickest premature babies from around the country. At present in Ireland there is no parental accommodation in Dublin, which means that parents have to pay for private accommodation or are separated from their baby. All the proceeds from this book will go directly into providing a permanent source of accommodation for parents while their babies are getting treatment.

Our charity Irish Premature Babies is run solely by volunteers. We rely on donations and fund-raising endeavours to provide support and care to families in need. If you would like to learn more about us, please visit us at www.irishprematurebabies.com.

Abbreviations

BiPAP   bi-level positive airway pressure
CPR   cardiopulmonary resuscitation
CLD   chronic lung disease
CPAP   continuous positive airway pressure
CUMH   Cork University Maternity Hospital
EBM   expressed breastmilk
GP   general practitioner
HDU   high-dependency unit
ICU   intensive-care unit
IUGR   intrauterine growth restriction
IUI   intrauterine insemination
IVF   in-vitro fertilisation
MRSA   Methicillin-resistant staphylococcus aureus
MRI   magnetic resonance imaging
NEC   necrotising enterocolitis
NICU   neonatal intensive care unit
NMH   National Maternity Hospital
PDA   patent ductus aerteriosus
PEG   percutaneous endoscopic gastrostomy
PFO   patent foramen ovale
PRS   Pierre Robin Syndrome
PND   post-natal depression
PET   pre-eclamptic toxaemia
PPROM   pre-term premature rupture of membranes
RDS   respiratory distress syndrome
RSV   respiratory syncytial virus
ROP   retinopathy of prematurity
SCBU   special care baby unit
TPN   total parenteral nutrition
TTTS   twin-to-twin transfusion syndrome
UV   ultraviolet

Glossary of Medical Terms

adenoidectomy surgical removal of the adenoids

anaemia the number of baby's red blood cells falls too low, making it harder for baby's bloodstream to deliver oxygen throughout the body

Apgar Score scale used to assess the well-being of a newborn baby at birth

apnoea episode when baby stops breathing for a period of 20 seconds or more

apnoea monitor item of equipment that helps detect irregularities or cessation of breathing

aspiration breathing any foreign matter or substance into the lungs, usually milk or meconium

bi-level positive airway pressure a breathing apparatus that helps get more air into the lungs

bili bed a protected incubator, exposed to fluorescent lights designed to emit in the blue spectrum to help flush out jaundice by phototherapy

bili lights a phototherapy tool to treat jaundice

blood culture a blood test to look for infection in the bloodstream

bradycardia a decrease or slowing of the heart rate, usually below 100 beats per minute in infants

breastmilk fortifier (BMF) a powder added to breastmilk for pre-term and small-for-gestational-age babies; BMFs contain extra energy, protein, vitamins and minerals to help the small baby grow better

bronchiolitis infection in the small airways of the lungs

bronchopulmonary dysplasia chronic lung disease associated with respiratory distress and ventilation

broviac line a central venous catheter used for long-term administration of substances via the venous system, such as antibiotics and total parenteral nutrition

cardiopulmonary resuscitation an emergency procedure in which the heart and lungs are made to work by manually compressing the chest overlying the heart and forcing air into the lungs

central line an intravenous line placed in the arm, groin or chest that extends up into a large blood vessel

cerebral palsy muscular and coordination problems as a result of a brain injury

chronic lung disease a condition in which damaged tissue in a newborn baby's lungs causes breathing and health problems

continuous positive airway pressure a system whereby air is blown continuously through baby's nose or endotracheal tube to help keep baby's lungs open between breaths. Used in situations where babies don't need full ventilator support but cannot breathe well enough on their own

cord prolapse a life-threatening obstetric emergency when the umbilical cord precedes the fetus's exit from the uterus

cyanosis bluish colour of the baby's skin usually caused by lack of oxygen

cytomegalovirus a virus that can cause birth defects or various medical problems for very premature babies; it can be passed from mother to baby during pregnancy

delayed myelination the development of the white matter of the myelin sheath is delayed for the baby's age and may cause concern or reasons for development delay

desats a drop in oxygen levels in the baby's bloodstream

electrocardiogram non-invasive and painless test that measures the electrical activity of the heart

electroencephalogram test that measures the electrical impulses of the brain

endotracheal tube tube placed in a baby's windpipe through his or her nose or mouth which delivers oxygen to the lungs

enteral feeding feeding using the gut, which can be given through the mouth as oral feeds or through a tube as tube-feeds

expressed breastmilk breastmilk which has been expressed by hand or pumped for babies who are unable to feed at the breast

extubation the removal of an endotracheal tube

feeding tube a thin catheter inserted into a baby's stomach through the mouth or nose to provide breastmilk or formula

full-term baby a baby born at 37 completed weeks' gestation

gavage feeding feeding delivered to the stomach via a gastric tube passed from the nose or mouth to the stomach

general practitioner a medical doctor who treats acute and chronic illnesses and provides preventive care and health education for all ages and both sexes

gestational age the number of weeks a baby is in the uterus

heart murmur an extra humming sound heard while examining the heart; it is often a normal finding in preemies but occasionally can be a sign of a heart defect

heel prick procedure in which a tiny prick is made on the heel in order to get a sample of blood for laboratory analysis to rule out a metabolic disorder

HELLP Syndrome a life-threatening obstetric complication usually considered to be a variant of pre-eclampsia whereby the patient has hemolysis (the breakdown of red blood cells) (H); elevated liver enzymes (EL) and low platelet (LP) count

high-dependency unit a step down from intensive care for patients requiring intermediate care

hydrocephalus a buildup of fluid inside the skull, leading to brain swelling

hyperemesis extreme, persistent nausea and vomiting in pregnancy

hypotonia a state of low muscle tone often involving reduced muscle strength

hypoxia temporary lack of sufficient oxygen in the baby's blood

ileostomy bag a bag that externally collects intestinal waste

incubator a specially designed temperature-regulated cot with a perspex cover which is used to provide warmth for pre-term babies and sick infants

infective endocarditis a form of inflammation of the inner tissue of the heart caused by infectious agents

intake volume of fluids and medications given through intravenous lines, or tube-feeds, or oral feed (e.g. breastfeeds or bottle-feeds)

intrauterine growth restriction poor growth of a baby while in the mother's womb during pregnancy; the developing baby weigh less than 90 per cent of other babies at the same gestational age

intrauterine insemination a procedure in which a fine tube is inserted through the opening of the womb to deposit a sperm sample inside

intravenous into a vein; fluids, drugs and food can be administered in this way

intraventricular haemorrhage bleeding within the ventricles in the brain

in-vitro fertilisation a laboratory procedure in which sperm is placed with an unfertilised egg in a Petri dish to achieve fertilisation; the embryo is then transferred into the uterus to begin a pregnancy or cryopreserved (frozen) for future use

jaundice yellow discoloration of the skin and whites of the eyes caused by build-up of bilirubin; it is predominantly due to immaturity of the liver and resolves as the baby matures

kangaroo care a method of caring for preemies that involves prolonged skin-to-skin contact

laryngomalacia a very common condition of infancy in which the soft, immature cartilage of the upper larynx collapses inward during inhalation, causing airway obstruction

low-birth-weight formula infant formula milk designed for preterm and small-for-gestational-age babies, which is fortified with extra energy, protein, vitamins and minerals to meet these babies' increased needs

lumbar puncture procedure whereby a needle is inserted between two vertebrae in the lower back below the end of the spinal cord to collect spinal fluid for testing

magnetic resonance imaging a medical imaging technique used to visualise detailed internal structures; makes use of the property of nuclear magnetic resonance to image nuclei of atoms inside the body

meconium material present in the fetal intestinal tract; usually excreted after birth but may be excreted *in utero* before the baby is born

meningitis an infection of the membrane surrounding the brain or spinal cord, which is diagnosed with a lumbar puncture or spinal tap to test the spinal fluid and treated with antibiotics

methicillin-resistant staphylococcus aureus a serious bacterial infection treated with antibiotics

monitor machine that records vital signs of heart rate, blood pressure and respiration

mucus plug a thick plug of mucus that gets stuck within the lungs and blocks airflow

myelination the formation of a sheath around a nerve to allow nerve impulses to move more quickly

nasogastric tube a thin rubber tube passed through nose down into the stomach to feed baby breastmilk or formula or to suction out excess stomach acid or mucus

necrotising enterocolitis a condition primarily seen in premature infants, where portions of the bowel undergo tissue death

neonatal intensive care unit 1 highest level of intensive care available for extremely sick, small babies in need of high-level specialist care

neonatal intensive care unit 2 next-to-highest level of intensive care, for babies still in need of high-level specialist care but who are in a stable condition

neonatalogy branch of paediatric medicine that deals with newborn babies

oligohydramnios decreased levels of amniotic fluid surrounding the baby

patent ductus aerteriosus a heart defect where the temporary maternal–fetal blood vessel does not close at birth

patent foramen ovale Normal opening between the left and right upper chambers of the heart fails to close naturally soon after birth

percutaneous endoscopic gastrostomy an procedure in which a tube is passed into a patient's stomach through the abdominal wall, most commonly to provide a means of feeding when oral intake is not adequate

periventricular leukomalacia a type of brain injury that affects infants, involving the death of small areas of brain tissue around fluid-filled areas called ventricles, due to inadequate blood circulation

phototherapy a jaundice treatment in which the blue range of light accelerates the excretion of bilirubin in the skin, decomposing it by photo-oxidation

Pierre Robin Syndrome a combination of birth defects which usually include a small lower jaw, cleft palate and a tendency for the tongue to 'ball up' in the back of the mouth, causing breathing and feeding problems

placenta previa a condition in which the placenta is too close to the cervix

placental haematoma an abnormal accumulation of maternal blood within or beneath the placenta or membranes

polycystic ovarian syndrome a condition in which an imbalance of a woman's female sex hormones can cause changes in the menstrual cycle, skin changes, small cysts in the ovaries, trouble getting pregnant and other problems

post-natal depression a form of clinical depression that can affect women after childbirth

pre-eclampsia a serious medical condition in which high blood pressure and protein in the urine develop after the 20th week (late second or third trimester) of pregnancy; also known as pre-eclamptic toxaemia

pre-term premature rupture of membranes the rupture of membranes prior to 37 weeks' gestation

pulmonary embolism a blockage of the main artery of the lung or one of its branches by a substance that has travelled from elsewhere in the body through the bloodstream

pulmonary haemorrhage an acute bleeding from the lung, especially in the upper respiratory tract

pyloric stenosis a narrowing of the opening from the stomach into the small intestine which causes severe vomiting in infants

respiratory distress syndrome a syndrome in premature infants caused by developmental insufficiency of surfactant production and structural immaturity in the lungs

respiratory syncytial virus a virus that causes a severe chest cold and wheezing

retinopathy of prematurity a weakening of the retina in young preemies that can cause long-term problems with vision and is corrected with laser surgery

rotavirus a virus causing severe, dehydrating and diarrhoea in infants and young children

sepsis a serious infection in the bloodstream that can affect various organs and cause complications; treated with antibiotics and intensive care

short bowel syndrome a condition in which nutrients are not properly absorbed due to severe intestinal disease or the surgical removal of a large portion of the small intestine

small for dates a term used for a baby born underweight for its gestation

special care baby unit (SCBU) babies are cared for in SCBU when their medical conditions stabilise and they are preparing for home; they receive extra nursing care and attention to help with gaining weight and learning to feed efficiently

surfactant substance produced in the lungs to assist lung function – often deficient in preemies, it can be administered through a tube to help improve immature lungs

tachycardia accelerated heart rate

total parenteral nutrition nutrition administered directly into a vein for babies unable to take their milk

transient tachypnea of the newborn a short, usually temporary, period of rapid breath after birth

twin-to-twin transfusion syndrome a condition that affects identical twin pregnancies whereby the shared placenta may be shared unequally and one twin's share may be too small to provide the necessary nutrients to grow normally or even to survive

ultraviolet light with wavelength shorter than that of visible light but longer than X-rays

ventilator any machine designed to mechanically move breathable air into and out of the lungs, to provide the mechanism of breathing for a patient physically unable to breathe or who is breathing insufficiently.

ventriculo-peritoneal shunt takes excess fluid from the fluid-filled cavities within the brain and diverts it to the abdomen for absorption

wing an area outside of intensive care where babies and parents become more 'hands on' with the baby's routine prior to getting home

Footprints

Dorothy Ferguson

How very softly you tiptoed into my world.
Almost silently,
Almost a moment you stayed.
But what an imprint
Your footsteps have left
Upon my heart.

ᔆ

Aaron McNally (rest in peace) (28 weeks), Amelia McNally (rest in peace) (25 weeks), Jessica McNally (32 weeks) and Sean Michael McNally (29 weeks)

At the age of 21, I discovered I was pregnant with my first baby. Katelyn was delivered at 33 weeks weighing 1.16 kg (2 lb 9 oz). She was in hospital for six weeks. She is eight now and getting her communion in May – Oh how time has flown by. Little did I realise when I had my daughter that special-care units would become a familiar place for me and my husband. For us as a couple, the time we spent in the Coombe's NICU will stay with us for ever.

Aaron was born at 28 weeks weighing 0.60 kg (1 lb 5 oz). I thought I knew so much about prematurity; after all, my daughter was also premature. How wrong I was. Aaron was so small – much smaller than my daughter, half her weight. He was ventilated and doing very little for himself. He was requiring the highest level of support and 100 per cent oxygen. He had several blood and platelet transfusions when I first saw him. The first thought in my head was fear . . . fear of everything. I was afraid he was in pain. I was afraid of all the pipes and tubes, one in his mouth and three from his belly button. I was afraid that he was going to die, and I was so afraid to love him. I tried so hard to not care for him because I knew how sick he was.

When Aaron was five days old, I was discharged from the hospital. His consultant asked for a word with me. She explained briefly that Aaron's left lung had collapsed and that he would require ventilation for a long time. She said he would have CLD too. I may have been told that he had a terminal disease as I did not know what this really bad disease was.

Every day I made the long trip to Dublin. (We live in Laois.) I sat beside Aaron's incubator, and time after time it was explained to me how sick he was. It was so hard. Every day I thought he was going to die. Every day I cried and cried and willed for him to live. I suppose the one emotion that I clinged on to at this stage was fear. I was still so afraid he was going to die, and I wished I did not love him so much. I cried when I was near him, I cried when I was away from him. I wanted him so much but I could not help him in any way. It was a hopeless situation.

This scenario continued for a long time. His biggest problem was his lungs. He needed high-frequency ventilation for a short period. Needing so much ventilation meant that he was mostly sedated. I rarely got to see him awake. He needed resuscitation on numerous occasions. It was just so scary. Aaron had 150 platelet transfusions and over 50 blood transfusions. He had so many marks from cannulas, and they had shaved most of his hair because access points were a problem. He had two central lines done in Crumlin and got infection after infection. He always needed antibiotics, and he even had a lumbar puncture as they felt infections may have spread.

After 11 long weeks, he was to be extubated – removed from the ventilator and put on nasal oxygen prongs. I was so excited. I would hear him cry for the first time, and he would be awake more often as he would not need the sedation he required when ventilated. I was told to go and have a coffee, and the extubation would be done during the rounds. I returned, and Aaron was on BiPAP. He was crying. He was so hoarse, kind of like a little cat. I sat and cried again. After 11 long weeks of ups and downs I was listening to my baby crying. I was so happy. He had turned a corner and was breathing on his own. He had been infection-free for nearly two weeks. I was just so happy.

When I returned the next day, Aaron had been changed to CPAP as he cried all day with BiPAP. Another step forward, it was great. Next step was nasal-prong oxygen, and he would more than likely leave the hospital needing oxygen. Then I got to feed him for the first time. He struggled, but after two or three attempts he seemed to be getting the hang of it. On Christmas Day (after 14 weeks in NICU), he was transferred into a cot and we were given a cubicle. I could not believe that we had come near the end of our journey. All we needed now was to get the hang of bottles and we were on the home stretch. The light at the end of the tunnel. Unfortunately this was not to be, and our little boy Aaron passed away in hospital at the age of four months.

One year later, I had my first and only term baby, Isabelle, who was 2.72 kg (6 lb). My fourth baby, Amelia, was born very early, at 25 weeks. I had an ultrasound at 8.20 a.m. It was discovered that the baby was in distress and her heart rate was very low. Within half an hour I was not pregnant: Amelia was delivered at 8.50 a.m., weighing 0.45 kg (1 lb). My mother, sister and husband rushed up. When nobody would tell me how the baby was I knew it was bad. I used all my strength to get out of bed and go up to the NICU to see her. She was a bad colour, really bruised around her head. I knew what this meant. She had a massive bleed on her brain. We awaited a cranial ultrasound to confirm our fears. Amelia had suffered four bleeds, two significant ones. She was doing nothing for herself. The doctors felt that it was best to let her go. We agreed, and she died 5 hours and 26 minutes after her birth. I came home with her a short while later.

I was very sad after Amelia's death, but I knew that I wanted another baby. Eleven months later I was back in the Coombe. I had Jessica at 32 weeks after a bad bleed. She was a good weight for her gestation: 1.9 kg (4 lb 3 oz). She did not breathe after delivery and required resuscitation for what felt like hours. She was then ventilated but was in a good condition. An hour later she was on CPAP and doing really well, and an hour after this she was breathing on her own. She spent two and a half weeks in SCBU. I was thrilled that we were coming home so soon. She had just begun to take her feeds and was back to birth weight.

Sean Michael was born at 29 weeks, weighing 1.27 kg (2 lb 13 oz). He needed CPAP to help him breathe as he had a partially collapsed lung and required ventilation for two days. He was taken off caffeine and started on tube-feeds. After four weeks, as the Coombe NICU was being renovated, he was moved to Portlaoise. There he continued to do well, and he is now a happy and healthy little boy.

For me, each experience in the NICU was very different. Each baby had his or her own battles, and each one turned out differently. There were a lot of tears and definitely a lot of fear. It is scary when you have a sick baby. It is also important not to compare one baby to another. Like all humans they are so different.

The staff are great, they try to help so much. Trust them: they know their jobs inside out. They care for the babies so well. They talk to them and even sing to them. They treat them just like normal babies. I learnt over time to put my trust in them. If you are in any doubt, ask questions. Ask all the questions you need to. If you don't understand, ask again. Do not leave the unit every day wondering what something means, just ask.

Photographs of Aaron McNally, Amelia McNally and Jessica McNally.

Aaron in the NICU before he passed away

A sister and father saying goodbye to a little sister and daughter

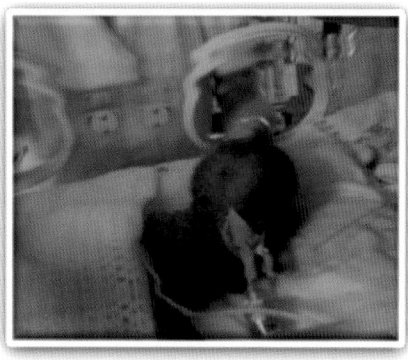
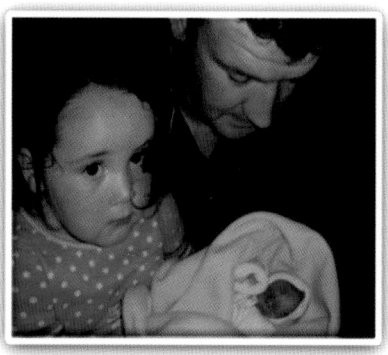

Little Jessica in the NICU

Big sisters Katelyn and Isabelle visiting Jessica

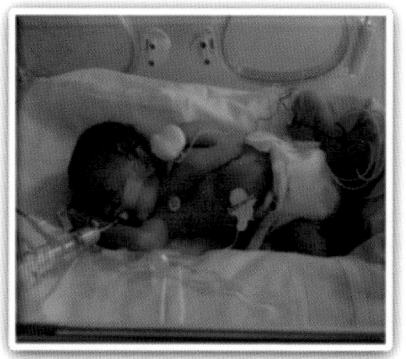

Abby Gaffney (28 weeks) and Katelyn Gaffney (32 weeks)

On my first pregnancy, I had problems with intermittent bleeding and was rushed by ambulance to Waterford Regional Hospital at 30 weeks. Katelyn hung on until 32 weeks, when I began to have contractions, and then my waters broke. It was determined to be premature labour as a result of an accident causing placental abruption. I am nothing if not pragmatic so when I was told she would be born soon, I asked if she was going to die. It was the worst moment of my life and I needed to ascertain what my baby's chances were. I asked, but didn't want to hear the answer. There was a good chance she would die, and if she survived it would be a long road home and I would always have to expect 'two steps forward, two steps back.' Happily, my little girl was delivered by emergency Caesarean section screaming. Two months early, she weighed 1.87 kg (4 lb 2 oz) and didn't require oxygen at birth. She had a nasogastric tube inserted but was breastfed as well. She didn't require any form of breathing assistance. The only medication she required was caffeine, for her heart. The NICU staff said she had an 'attitude'. Eventually she was transferred to Kilkenny to be closer to us at home. They said she was a miracle baby because she just kept going forward. She spent just over three weeks in hospital. At nine months, Katelyn had a check-up with her paediatricians, and, as she was crawling and starting to talk, they deemed her to no longer need paediatric care related to her prematurity. It was one of the proudest days of my life.

Abby was born at 28 weeks. As before, my pregnancy was problematic. Things appeared to be stabilising until one

Tiny Footprints

morning my Braxton Hicks intensified and were coming two minutes apart. I also had the familiar dragging pain from hipbone to hipbone I'd had with my two previous labours. In hospital, I discovered I was having regular contractions but with no internal progress, i.e. effectively I was not in labour. I had steroid injections administered at 4.00 p.m. to start maturing the baby's lungs. The contractions calmed; however, I started to lose large clumps of tissue which were sent for analysis to determine their histology. I spent the afternoon and night on pethedine for the pain of my contractions, and at 4.00 a.m. I received the second steroid injection. Ten minutes later I started to experience indescribable pain, worse than I had ever had before in my life. I had a massive vaginal bleed and lost tissue in fist-size proportions. The pain I was experiencing was dilation occurring extremely rapidly. An emergency section under general anaesthetic was ordered as I was haemorrhaging. All I wanted was for my baby to live and to be able to see her.

In recovery, I was told that Abby was fine and was being transferred to Dublin. My mother organised for me to be transferred to the NMH in Dublin with my baby. I visited Abby as much as ward rounds afforded. I touched her, stroked her and told her how much I loved her. When I was resting in my hospital bed, I cried because she was in the NICU, in a plastic box, when she should have been at home with her parents who loved her so much.

We learnt to judge our child's well-being by tracking numbers: saturate levels, heart rate, oxygen percentages, minutes breathing unassisted. Whilst parents of full-term infants watch their baby sleep and hold and feed them, all information regarding our child was obtained over the phone and in those all-important numerical formats.

When Abby was transferred back to Waterford Regional Hospital, she came off oxygen quite quickly, but she experienced difficulties with feeding. Her stomach would bloat massively, her feed would be withdrawn, and she would be put back on a drip. The worst-case scenario was that she had serious gastrointestinal issues, but fortunately it was just wind. Abby didn't take to bottle-feeding straight away despite the constant coaxing – just one more setback on the road to getting her home.

One day, she took to the bottle, and from that point her days in hospital were numbered. Nine weeks and six days after she was born, Abby came home. We spent the first night just watching her sleep. Abby is 10 months old and has no health problems at all. She is like every other seven-month-old baby and has just cut her first teeth. I believe I'm so fortunate. So much could have been wrong, but it has turned out so right. My children are so wonderful, true fighters who wouldn't be as they are today were it not for their prematurity.

Photographs of Abby Gaffney and Katelyn Gaffney.

Abby holding on, just two days old

Katelyn in the NICU

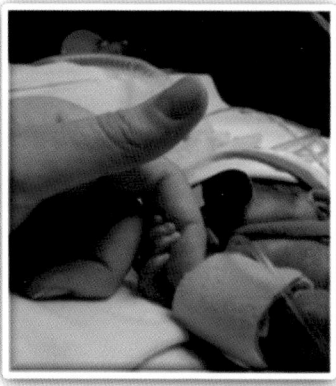

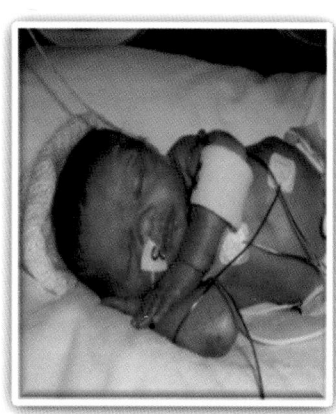

Abby at nine months

Katelyn at two years

ॐ

Adam Butler and Alex Butler (28 weeks)

I was 20 weeks pregnant when I learnt I was having twins. Shock turned to excitement and then to fear when the consultant told me that they were identical and sharing a placenta and that twin 2 seemed to be a lot smaller than twin 1. He decided to refer me to Professor Fergal Malone in the Royal College of Surgeons Ireland based in the Rotunda Hospital in Dublin. At this appointment, Professor Malone confirmed what my consultant in Clonmel had told me. He went on to say that the blood flow to twin 2's cord was reduced and that I would have to be admitted from 24 weeks until the babies were born. I have three other children at home so this was going to be very difficult. Two weeks later, at 24 weeks, I travelled to Dublin, upset to be leaving my children at home and worried about my unborn babies. I was given steroid injections to develop the babies' lungs and was told I would have an ultrasound twice a week and regular traces of the babies' hearts.

On 19 April, as I stood up, I felt a gush of water. The doctor examined me and told me that I was leaking fluid. I was put on antibiotics and monitored closely for the next 48 hours. I was terrified but luckily the babies hung on. Then, on 24 April, as I was examined by the doctor, it was discovered that the remaining fluid around the babies was stained with meconium. The babies would have to be delivered by emergency Caesarean section. The NICU in the Rotunda Hospital was full so I would have to be transferred to the NMH, on the far side of Dublin city. I phoned my partner to explain what was happening, and he frantically tried to sort out childcare and made his way up to Dublin, not having a clue how to get to Holles Street.

Tiny Footprints

I was transferred by ambulance, and when I arrived the team was waiting for me. I was put on a monitor, examined and brought to theatre. On 25 April, at 28 weeks' gestation, Alex was born weighing 1.43 kg (3 lb 2oz), and Adam arrived two minutes later weighing 0.86 kg (1 lb 14 oz). We got a glimpse of our babies before they were rushed up to the NICU, but it wasn't until the next morning that we got to see them properly. That first visit to the NICU was petrifying: our tiny babies were on ventilators and hooked up to all sorts of drips and machines. We got to touch them through the doors of the incubators. The hospital chaplin asked us if we would like to have the boys blessed, and we did.

On day 2 we got to hold our babies – an unforgettably happy experience amidst all the fear and uncertainty. We were told that the results of the boys' cranial ultrasounds had come back. Adam's was clear but Alex's was showing up something. It didn't seem to be a bleed, but it looked like it may have been caused by an infection or lack of oxygen in the womb and could potentially cause problems later on with his mobility, especially in the lower limbs. Both boys were taken off ventilators and put on CPAP. At this point Adam wasn't tolerating tube-feeds at all, and the doctor was concerned about NEC. Thankfully, he didn't have NEC, but he did have a blood infection and was put on antibiotics.

Meanwhile, Alex was really coming on and was taken off CPAP and put on nasal-prongs oxygen. Adam still wasn't improving so they did a lumbar puncture. The results were terrifying. He had meningitis and was put on more antibiotics for 21 days. There was a real possibility that the infection could cause brain damage, but thankfully the scans came back clear. Over the next few days, Alex came on really well. He was taken off oxygen, started on bottle-feeds and moved to the SCBU. We discussed transferring him to Clonmel but decided to wait until Adam was well enough so that we could move them together. The boys were transferred to South

Tipperary General Hospital on 3 June. At this stage Alex had his feeding tube removed and he was completely off oxygen. Adam was off CPAP but still needed oxygen and would have to be weaned off slowly as he had developed CLD. On 10 June Alex came home after 46 days. Adam was still being slowly weaned off oxygen and introduced to bottle-feeds but finally, after 77 days, he came home. Our boys were together at last. They have been through so much. They are our little miracles.

Photographs of Adam Butler and Alex Butler.

Adam, just one day old

Alex, just one day old

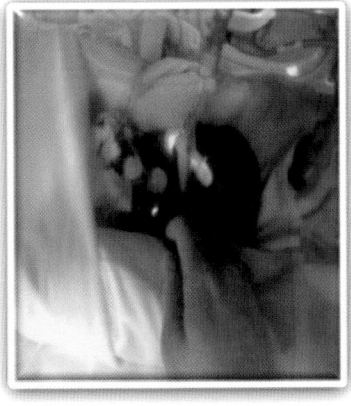

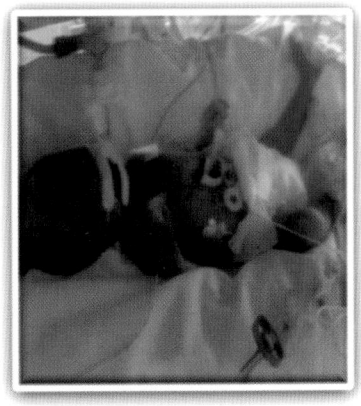

Adam and Alex reunited in the SCBU at five weeks

Home together at long last at 11 weeks

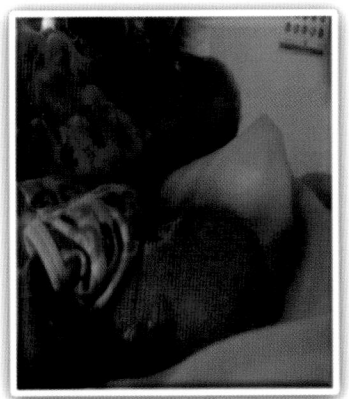

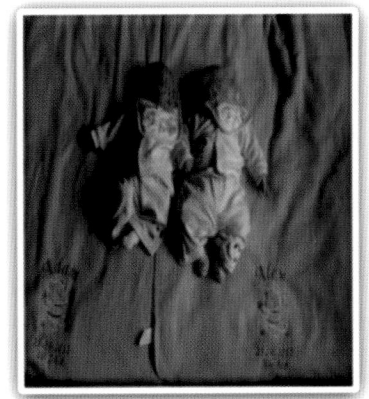

Adam Finnegan and Daniel Finnegan
(27 weeks)

After an eventful pregnancy involving numerous hospital stays, my identical twin boys, Adam and Daniel, put in an early appearance on 1 April at 27 weeks and 4 days at the NMH in Dublin. They were immediately taken to the NICU. Unfortunately neither my husband Mick nor I caught a glimpse of them. Adam weighed 1.04 kg (2 lb 4 oz) and Daniel a tiny 0.88 kg (1 lb 15 oz).

Both boys were ventilated almost straight away as I had not been given any drugs to mature their tiny lungs. After an agonising night not being able to see them, I was finally brought up to the NICU the next morning, which was a traumatic and terrifying experience to say the least. Nothing can prepare you for the sights and sounds of the NICU, and the sight of my tiny boys fighting for their lives was heartbreaking. This was not how motherhood should be.

The boys were as stable as they could be for the first 48 hours of their lives, and all we could do was sit and watch them. The first week passed by in a blur, and we were updated daily as to their progress and the potential problems that faced us. It was soon discovered that Daniel had developed a heart murmur and would need surgery to close a valve in his heart. This was carried out in Our Lady's Children's Hospital, Crumlin, when he was 27 days old and was probably the worst day we had experienced up to then. A few days later he was also found to have an intraventricular haemorrhage on his brain, which thankfully regressed. Both boys suffered many infections, needed blood transfusions and had suspected

Tiny Footprints

meningitis. Adam developed ROP, which has also thankfully corrected itself.

After what seemed like a lifetime, the boys left the NICU for the SCBU. They made good progress and continued to gain weight in the SCBU. Finally, on 27 June (their due date), they were allowed home. Things at home were very hard in the beginning but eventually it became easier and the boys began to thrive. As the years have passed, Adam and Daniel have been slow to achieve milestones but have eventually done so. Today, at eight years of age, they are perfectly healthy and happy boys, with no ill effects from their traumatic start in life. We feel blessed and extremely lucky to have them in our lives.

Photographs of Adam Finnegan and Daniel Finnegan.

Adam, just two days old

Daniel, fighting for his survival

Adam and Daniel having a cuddle with Mam.

The boys on holiday in the UK in 2010

ℂℛ

Adam Hayes (28 weeks)

When I saw the sonographer's expression change during my 28-week scan, I knew that something was wrong. My baby had stopped growing, and blood flow to the placenta was greatly reduced. I was given steroid injections immediately. My baby was extremely small. Twelve hours after I had my second steroid shot I was scanned to count the baby's movements. I will never forget it. It was 8.00 a.m., the consultant and I were the only two people in the fetal assessment area of the hospital, and in 10 minutes my baby had only lethargically moved an arm so she rushed me out of the scanning area and started shouting for people to get me ready for theatre.

I didn't get a chance to phone my husband and tell him what was happening. I was so terrified. When I got to theatre they failed to locate the baby's heartbeat with a Doppler and had to perform an immediate Caesarean section before the spinal block took hold. My son Adam arrived into the world, weighing 0.74 kg (1 lb 10 oz). He was rushed off to the NICU and I didn't get to see him until 36 hours later. When I saw him for the first time I felt sick as he did not look like a baby. He was covered in wires, bruises and dried blood, and we couldn't see his face. His first week was horrific. Every moment we weren't with him we were waiting for the phone call to say he had died.

Adam spent two weeks on a ventilator, three weeks on CPAP and six weeks on oxygen prongs. He had a couple of infections, two bleeds on the brain and three blood transfusions. He had to be resuscitated twice and suffered numerous bradycardias – all of which are common in premature babies. He needed double hernia surgery. Adam was in University College Hospital in Galway for 11 weeks and in Our Lady's Children's Hospital in Crumlin for one week.

I was diagnosed with a blood-clotting condition known as Factor V Leiden, which causes blood to clot more than it should. The placenta was full of clots, and my baby was being starved. Thankfully he was delivered when he was, as the more usual outcome with this condition is stillbirth. Adam is the smartest, funniest boy who lights up our lives. He suffers recurrent chest infections, and steroids and inhalers are his constant companions, but apart from the scars on his hands and feet you would never know the hardship our miracle boy has been through.

Photographs of Adam Hayes.

Adam, just two days old   *Adam, 10 days old*

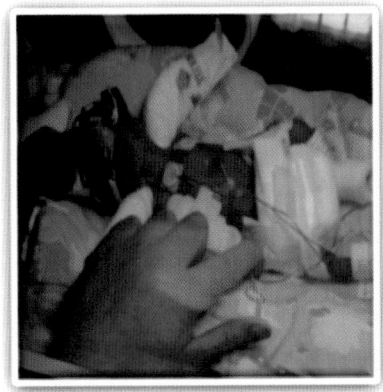
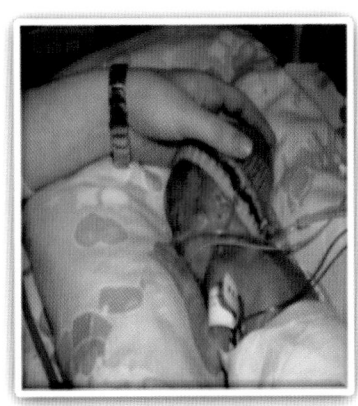

Adam at nine months   *Adam at four years, all grown up*

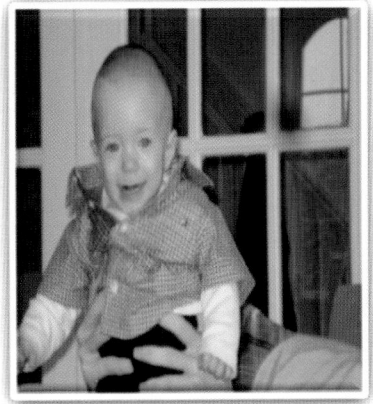

CR

Adam Keye and Nathan Keye (33 weeks)

After almost five years of Clomid (a fertility drug), multiple injectable cycles, three IUIs, five courses of IVF, a miscarriage and an ectopic pregnancy, we were delighted to find out we were having twins. Our family was finally to be complete. Never for one second did we think of all the complications that can go with a twin pregnancy, let alone all the bottles and nappies.

It was week 28 when a sense of reality kicked in, after I was admitted with pre-eclampsia. At 33 weeks, a Caesarean section was booked, and Adam was born at 3.03 p.m. on 3 November weighing 1.9 kg (4 lb 3 oz). Nathan duly followed at 3.04 p.m. weighing 1.56 kg (3 lb 7 oz). We were ecstatic as they both seemed so robust and healthy. Only moments later though both boys were in incubators and Adam began to struggle for oxygen. I was blissfully unaware of the seriousness of the situation, but Nick my husband was in the room and can remember the sensation of helplessness and the sight of Nathan all alone as everyone worked on Adam. It wasn't long before Adam passed through the simpler stages of intervention and was rushed to an NICU in a larger hospital. He had the worst case of RDS the consultant had seen in 20 years and remained in a critical state for over a week.

Nathan was doing relatively well in the SCBU; he was being tube-fed and required occasional oxygen but would spontaneously stop breathing from time to time to keep everyone on their toes.

Over the weeks, Adam grew stronger and stronger and went down through the ranks of the unit and the equipment. From NICU to HDU and eventually to the SCBU and from the ventilator to CPAP to oxygen in the incubator. Just as we thought he was ready for transfer back to the original hospital he was diagnosed with a PDA. Thankfully after numerous tests, cardiology reviews and patience, it resolved itself, and he did not require surgery.

My days went by in a bit of a haze, rushing from one hospital to the other, expressing milk at all times of the day and night, at home and in both hospitals. I used the bilateral pump and remember feeling a bit like a cow on a milking machine. However, as I felt so useless, expressing seemed to be the only thing I could do for my boys and a way of maintaining some control over the situation. As time went on Nathan was allowed out of the incubator for longer periods so I was able to care for him, change his nappy and tube-feed him. Adam, on the other hand, was hooked up to so many machines it was over two weeks before I was allowed to hold him. I remember the nurse asking for the first time if I wanted to do kangaroo care and I was terrified. He was still so sick, with tubes everywhere, but when she eventually settled him on my chest all those fears just melted and I truly felt like his mother.

After six weeks he was transferred back to his original hospital and we were reunited briefly again. Nathan was discharged home two weeks before Adam. It was another tough day, taking one baby home with us and leaving another behind. We did, however, have both boys at home with us for their first Christmas.

There were some comparatively minor hurdles when we got home. Nathan suffered severe acid reflux. He was in such pain, screaming for hours and arching his back and could not lie flat. Constant feeding soothed him but also aggravated the condition so finding a balance was difficult and definitely nerve-wracking. We invested in every product and every remedy we could find, from pillow wedges to thickened feeds. My husband Nick used to spend evenings driving between different pharmacies – searching for different remedies according to him, searching for a few minutes' peace in my mind. We resorted to using an apnoea monitor for months so that Nathan could get some relief from his reflux by sleeping on his tummy.

Adam had hypotonia (low muscle tone) and attended physiotherapy for six months. We were told by the physiotherapist that he might have cerebral palsy. We had to do a series of exercises every nappy change along with special floor-time activities to help strengthen his muscles. I remember being worried about every milestone that Nathan reached before Adam.

They are now two and a half, very happy, healthy and funny little boys. The story of their arrival into this world feels like it happened to someone else now and so very long ago.

Photographs of Adam Keye and Nathan Keye.

Adam on a ventilator

Nathan holding on to Mommy

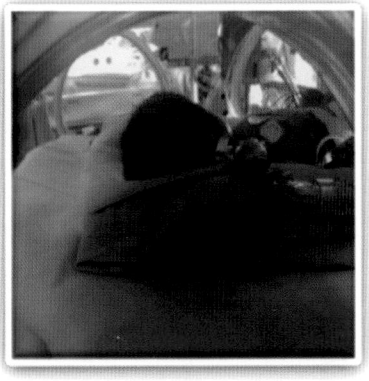

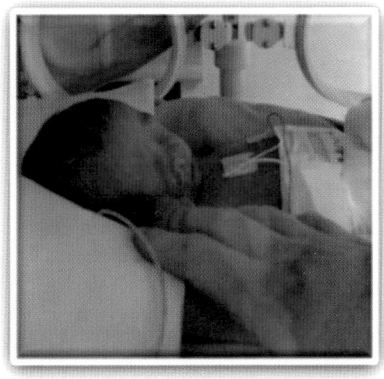

Adam's and Nathan's first day at home

Adam and Nathan at two and a half, playing

Aine McGinn and Aoifa McGinn (33 weeks)

When I found out I was pregnant with identical twins I was terrified. I was warned of all the possible complications from the beginning, the two most common being TTTS and premature labour. All scans were uneventful until 23 February when my doctor discovered fluid in the abdomen of baby B. I was referred to the Rotunda Hospital in Dublin for an urgent scan three days later. My mother accompanied me. I knew straight away something was very wrong when I heard the following: 'Too much fluid, baby B, no fluid around baby A, heart failure baby B, organ failure baby A', and it went on and on and on. That's when they said it was TTTS stage 4. I had to have laser surgery straight away to save the babies. The surgery involved putting a camera with a laser attached into my womb and zapping the blood vessels connecting the two babies on the surface of the placenta. I was awake for the whole procedure. That's when I found out they were girls. I had the rarest of experiences in that I saw my babies in the womb on the screen. It was like watching the National Geographic channel. The surgery was a success, and the babies thrived. I had weekly scans until 24 May when I went into premature labour at 33 weeks and 2 days.

I had an emergency C-section, and Aine was born first, weighing 2.13 kg (4 lb 11 oz) followed 30 seconds later by Aoifa, weighing 2.52 kg (5 lb 9 oz). Doctors were amazed by their weights. They were the biggest children in the NICU. I was so shocked when I first saw them attached to monitors and drips but was reassured by the cardiologist who told me that their little hearts were fine after the TTTS. The nurses were fantastic and explained everything to me and put me at ease.

Even though they were such a good size, they did not have the sucking reflex and had to be tube-fed for two weeks. During the feeds they were given a soother to associate sucking with feeding. They remained on monitors until they could suck a bottle and were over 2.72 kg (6 lb). When I was discharged and the girls were not, leaving them behind me in Dublin was one of the hardest things I have ever had to do. I rang every day, and the nurses were amazing.

I had to try and synchronise my visits with their feeding. For one week, they remained in Dublin before being transferred to the Midland Regional Hospital. Being at a hospital nearer to home made it easier for me to breastfeed them. We were thrilled to have them one step closer to home and extremely lucky to have the SCBU within easier commuting distance. The girls remained in the SCBU for two weeks. They put on weight and started demand feeding. Every time they cried for a feed was one step closer to bringing them home. The nurses were fantastic, allowing me unlimited access to the girls, and they were so reassuring. I gave them their first bath in Portlaoise; they were so tiny I was terrified. I also got to dress them and change their nappies. This was the first time I felt like their mammy.

Once they were transferred from their incubators into cots I knew it would not be long before they were home. They got fed up of being tube-fed, and Aine pulled out her tube first, followed one hour later by Aoifa. The nurses left the tubes out, and they went on demand feeding for 48 hours. Three days later, I got the phone call I had been waiting for. The girls were coming home. They came home on 14 June, at three weeks of age, and got to meet their big brother for the first time. Being only two years old he did not understand that Mammy was bringing home two new babies.

We got them into a great routine early, and both were sleeping through the night by eight weeks. Even though I had two tiny babies I was much more relaxed with them because it was my second time being a mammy. They are one now and are in the 90th percentile of development. Aine has now developed mild pulmonary valve stenosis, a side effect of TTTS, and attends Our Lady's Children's Hospital, Crumlin, but apart from that they are thriving.

Photographs of Aine McGinn and Aoifa McGinn.

Aine, day 2

Aoifa, day 2

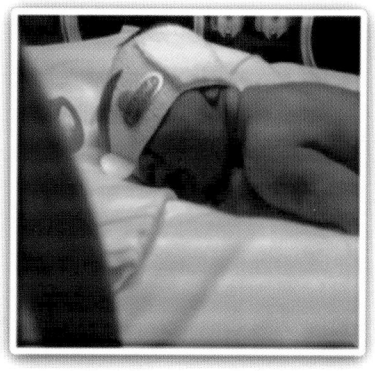

Aine and Aoifa at six months

The girls at one on the beach

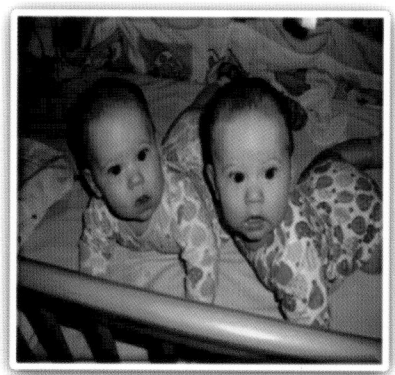

Aisling Haines (34 weeks), Aoife Haines (34 weeks) and Conor Haines (30 weeks)

I had my son Conor at almost 31 weeks on 20 November, weighing 1.45 kg (3 lb 3 oz). My due date was the end of January, and I remember thinking wouldn't it be nice if he came in time for Christmas – little did I know. The day he was born was the best but also the scariest day of my life. I woke up bleeding heavily, and we rushed in to the NMH in Dublin city in rush-hour traffic. I think we made it from our home in Bray, Co. Wicklow, in less than 15 minutes. After a few stressful hours, Conor was born around lunch-time by Caesarean section. I got a brief look at him before he was whisked up to NICU. Lying in recovery was surreal. I had gone from being pregnant to suddenly lying in a hospital room with no bump and no baby beside me, and I just couldn't take it all in. When I saw him that evening he was in an incubator and on CPAP, so I could barely see his little face.

That week was such a roller-coaster. I was up and down the stairs to the NICU. I was pumping to establish a good supply and sitting beside Conor's incubator with tears streaming down my face. He was struggling to cope with being fed and was managing only about 3 ml of EBM in his tube-feeds before vomiting. Leaving the hospital without him felt so wrong, and I only managed a few hours at home before rushing back in to see him. In total, he spent five weeks in hospital, and every day had its highs and lows. I would ring the hospital in the morning to find out how he had been and then go in and spend the day sitting beside him and having precious kangaroo cuddles. My day ended with another call to the nurses before I could relax and go to sleep. My heart would be in my mouth before pushing the door open to the NICU as so much could change in such a short period of time. In a way, time stood still while Conor was in hospital, as it was easy to lose all interest in the outside world.

From day 1 we had hoped Conor would be home for Christmas, and he did everything he could, taking all his bottles and reaching 1.8 kg (3 lb 15 oz) just in time. We were told he could come home three days before Christmas, and we rushed in to get him only to find him back on IV fluids as he was not coping well with increasing feeds. The doctor then said maybe Christmas Eve, and again we ran in like excited children to collect him, but another doctor disagreed, and he was kept in. We woke up on Christmas morning heavy-hearted and so disappointed not to have him at home with us, but when we got to the hospital we were told he could go home. We rang our family and told them to set an extra place for dinner and practically ran out of the hospital in case the doctors changed their minds. We still tell Conor that he was the best Christmas present ever and that Santa made an extra-special delivery that year.

The following Christmas I found out I was pregnant again and later discovered it was twins. My pregnancy went well, but at 34 weeks my waters broke, and Aoife and Aisling were born weighing 2.07 kg (4 lb 9 oz) and 2.13 kg (4 lb 11 oz). The girls spent two weeks in special care, which I found even harder the second time. They were a lot bigger and stronger than their brother and looked huge to me. I really felt that all would be fine if we could just bring them home. I did not care if we were feeding them around the clock as long as they were with us. Aoife was ready to go home first, and it was so upsetting to think of Aisling being left in hospital without her sister. Eventually the staff agreed that we could bring them together, as they knew that we had been through it all before with Conor.

They have each had their share of hospital appointments and developmental checks and thankfully now are healthy, happy toddlers with no issues. They are so far removed from the tiny babies that we welcomed into the world, but every now and then I have a look at the tiny clothes they wore just to remind me of how precious they are.

Photographs of Aisling Haines, Aoife Haines and Conor Haines.

Aoife and Aisling, one week old, having cuddles with Daddy

Conor, just one day old

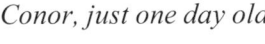

Conor, five weeks old with Mammy

Aoife, Aisling and Conor together in June 2011

CR

Alex O'Driscoll (30 weeks)

My story begins at 13 weeks into my pregnancy. I had a bleed and went to the hospital to get checked, and from then until 24 weeks I had a threatening miscarriage. When I reached week 24 of my pregnancy I was given the steroid injections to develop my baby's lungs. At 26 weeks, my waters broke, and this was when my whole world was turned upside down. I had been admitted into hospital because of the risk of infection. I had a five-year-old at home missing her mum and a mum missing her daughter. CUMH was to become my temporary home for the next couple of weeks.

On 17 November, at 9.15 p.m., my temperature started to rise, and I started getting labour pains. I was taken to the HDU. I met with my consultant, who decided to deliver my baby by Caesarean section. I rang my partner to come to the hospital as soon as possible. While I was getting prepped for surgery, the staff was unable to administer the spinal epidural, so it was decided that I had to have a general anaesthetic. When I woke up, I remember being frantic, looking for my baby boy Alex and my partner. Thankfully the staff brought me to see them both in the NICU. I later learnt that Alex was born at 1.03 a.m. and weighed 1.47 kg (3 lb 4 oz), which was not bad considering he was 10 weeks early.

Alex was born with jaundice and *E. coli*. This is what had caused my PPROM. He was put on CPAP for two days and then came off it as he was doing so well. On New Year's Eve, he contracted a viral infection, and he suffered respiratory failure. He was then put back on CPAP. For the next eight weeks Alex went through a roller-coaster of good and bad days. He had regular apnoeas and bradycardias, which are very distressing for parents to witness. He had numerous infections and had to get antibiotics, but thankfully he fought them all. On 12 January we finally got to take our little man Alex home. He is doing really well at home now. He is eight months old and is gaining good weight.

Photographs of Alex O'Driscoll.

Alex, just three days old

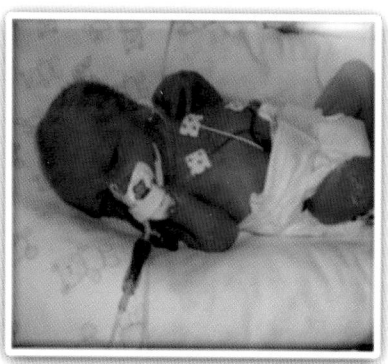

Alex, promoted to a cot, with a little friend to keep him company

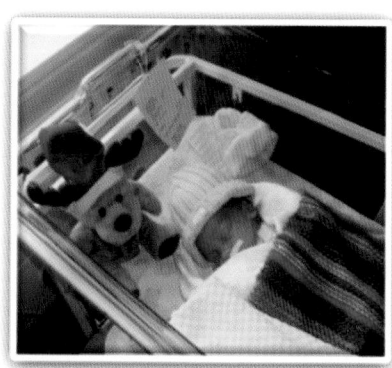

Alex, ready for Christmas and almost ready for home

Alex at seven and a half months

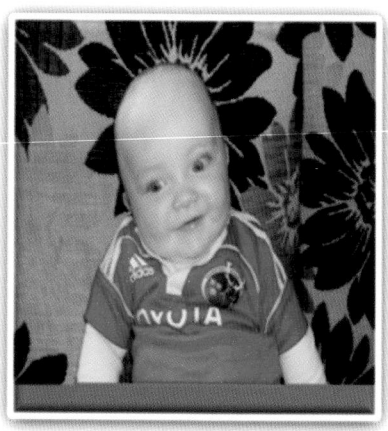

Alva Trehy (33 weeks) and Cian Trehy (28 weeks)

Our second child Cian arrived while we were on a week's holiday in Lanzarote, four years ago. He was born at 28 weeks, weighing 1.26 kg (2 lb 12 oz). I'd had a perfectly normal, complication-free pregnancy, and my doctor sanctioned me to travel on holiday. My first baby Keira had arrived only three weeks early so I was in no way worried. I woke early on the Thursday morning with stomach pains which I put down to food poisoning or something I had eaten the previous night and continued to get ready for the wedding we were attending that day. But the pains gradually got worse. Just as we were about to leave I knew it was something more serious. We rushed to the local hospital with our nearly-two-year-old girl, where I was advised that I was already 5 cm dilated. The baby was arriving. I was told by a doctor that the prognosis was not good. I was in shock as I had never heard of a baby being born that early before.

Cian arrived shortly after in a room full of medical staff speaking Spanish, so I didn't know what was going on. A few minutes later we got to see him before he was taken by helicopter to an NICU in Tenerife. His dad flew to Tenerife on the Thursday evening, and between checking on the baby, who was critical, and sorting out flights and accommodation for us it was a hectic time. Three days after the birth, the day after I was discharged from hospital, we all flew to Tenerife. Our little girl was constantly screaming and refused to eat or sleep as she knew something major had happened but could not understand what. Upon landing, the hospital rang and said to come in immediately as things were not looking good. We rushed straight there, and when I saw Cian's tiny body on high-frequency ventilation, I nearly passed out.

Cian fought on through infection after infection, a number of blood transfusions with needles in all his tiny little veins and machines constantly on the go. He was ventilated for four weeks, and I eventually got to hold him then, which was such an emotional moment. He also got NEC and two bleeds in his brain, one of which resulted in hydrocephalus (fluid around the brain). At four weeks, he had an operation to insert a sac in his head to drain fluid from his brain manually each day.

Over the next few days, Cian stopped breathing a number of times so once his weight exceeded the 1.36 kg (3 lb) mark they operated on him to insert a permanent shunt to drain the excess fluid from his brain. The shunt will remain in situ permanently and will require continuous monitoring. Once the shunt was in, Cian turned a corner and was swiftly moved to special care to focus on his feeding.

Seven weeks after he first entered the world, his paediatrician, Dr Angel (Angel by name and by nature) told us he was ready for the journey home. After many calls to the insurance company, the air ambulance was arranged, and my little man and I were on our way home at last. We were transferred to the NMH in Dublin. He was doing so well then that they discharged him the next morning when he was only 2.07 kg (4 lb 9 oz) and just over eight weeks old.

Four years on, and with all the usual hospital check-ups, he is doing fantastic. He has had a couple of overnight stays in hospital to monitor his shunt, but it has always been fine. He also has weak muscles in his legs that he has just started physiotherapy for, but he is in playschool, has lots of friends and is a clever, affectionate little boy.

He now also has a little sister, Alva, who arrived at 33 weeks in December 2009. I had an emergency Caesarean section on my third child and subsequently found out that I have a bicornate (heart-shaped) uterus, which is the reason for

Tiny Footprints

my premature labours. This removed some of the guilt that I was feeling as I now knew that neither the flight nor carrying my other child had contributed to Cian's premature birth.

When we got home from Spain, I met up with some of the parents from an Irish parenting website, and it was fantastic to speak to other parents as in Spain nobody spoke English and I had no Spanish. At times it was very confusing and frustrating, and meeting up with the parents back here was a huge support. I am so glad that Irish Premature Babies are now here to help and support other parents through some of the trauma of having a premature baby.

Photographs of Alva Trehy and Cian Trehy.

Cian, just one week old   Cian having fun aged one

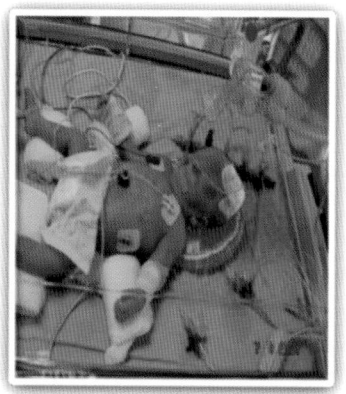

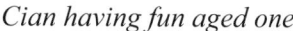

Alva playing away   Alva and Cian with big sister
                           Keira

❧

Amelia Beale (rest in peace) and Luke Beale (24 weeks)

After many years waiting and hoping to become pregnant, we were overjoyed that we were – and not only that, it was twins. The pregnancy progressed normally, we had many scans of our babies and resisted the urge to find out if they were boys or girls. I relished planning and organising all the things we needed for them. Then the day I hit 24 weeks I started having pains and decided to go to the NMH in Holles Street, Dublin. It was the beginning of the most frightening time of our lives.

After being examined, the doctor told us our babies were coming that day. We couldn't believe it. We just kept repeating that it was way too early. Another doctor from the NICU came to explain to us all the problems they could face if they survived and that it was going to be a very long and difficult journey. Our daughter Amelia was born first at 8.35 p.m., weighing 0.74 kg (1 lb 10 oz), and Luke followed four minutes later weighing 0.72 kg (1 lb 10 oz). Both were rushed to the NICU, with us barely getting a glimpse of our babies.

The first few days were an overwhelming mix of emotions, seeing our babies so tiny and covered with so many wires, trying to absorb all the information we were being given and feeling completely useless as we couldn't do anything for them. We had been told the prognosis may not be good, but we kept trying to hope for the best. As they made it into their fourth day, our worst fears were realised when Amelia became very ill. The team looking after her told us she wasn't going to survive. It was impossible to hear and take in. We couldn't believe our child was going to be taken from us. We held her, spoke to her and brought her to her brother to say goodbye. Later that night she passed away in our arms. It was completely devastating.

Watching Luke put up such a fight for his life gave us the strength to face everything ahead of us. Luke showed everyone his amazing fighting spirit. He was still very ill when Amelia passed away, and we couldn't cope with the thought of losing him too. He faced a huge struggle, with his weight dropping to 0.65 kg (1 lb 7 oz) and his lungs being so damaged. Every day we would sit with him, praying that he would get stronger and put on some weight. Every gram gained felt like a huge step forward. He was on a ventilator for eight weeks. During this time his lungs became very scarred. He fought off many infections and lung collapses. Watching him have to be resuscitated on a daily basis was petrifying. The day he finally made it off the ventilator was a very special day for us all. He was moved onto CPAP and other oxygen providers for the rest of his time in hospital.

Eighteen days after he was born we finally got to hold him. It was the most amazing feeling for both of us to finally hold our son. Every day we watched our little boy slowly get stronger and fight against all the setbacks. Milestones, like finally watching him open his eyes, gave us such hope. We would sit with him, talk to him and hold him, getting used to the beeping alarms and the machines. Being able to do normal things, such as changing his nappy and feeding him, felt like the most amazing privilege. Just as it looked like he was doing really well Luke got MRSA and was moved to isolation. Again he put up a great fight, and we finally got to take him home just before his due date. He was four months and weighing a huge 2.78 kg (6 lb 2 oz).

Taking Luke home was amazing, but we were also petrified leaving the support of the hospital behind. Luckily we had incredible support from our families, and watching them finally get to meet Luke was amazing. We settled in at home, enjoying having our son with us, and kept very busy with all of the follow-up appointments. We received fantastic support from all the medical team monitoring his development. Luke has beaten all the odds and is now an amazing five-year-old little boy. He has faced every obstacle put in his path with his usual determination. He is completely healthy now and is starting school this September. He is without doubt an amazing little boy, and we know how lucky we are to have him. We will never stop missing our daughter Amelia, and we have told Luke he has a special angel watching over him. Although we would give anything for our daughter to be with us, we know she is doing an incredible job looking after her twin brother.

Photographs of Amelia Beale and Luke Beale.

Amelia, four days old

Luke, six days old

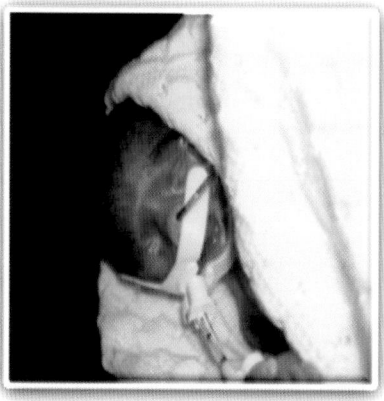

Luke, 75 days in isolation

The most handsome Luke at five years old

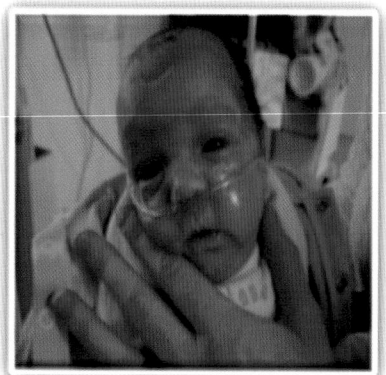

Tiny Footprints

Amelia McDermott (25 weeks)

After 13 weeks of unexplained bleeding and several emergency-room attendances, my labour commenced on day 6 of week 25 of my pregnancy. My daughter Amelia was delivered by emergency Caesarean section weighing 0.78 kg (1 lb 12 oz). She required resuscitation, was administered the life-saving drug surfactant for her lungs, was intubated and taken to the NICU where she would spend the next 77 days. And so began the journey of endless handwashing to the point of drawing blood, alarm bells ringing in my dreams, tiny babies clinging to life by a thread and the parallel world of the NICU.

The initial days of Amelia's life were fraught with uncertainty, fear, loss and a bizarre sense of jubilation. Amelia's condition remained critical for seven weeks during which time she suffered from a PDA, which was medicated and closed over. She had lung secretions which required removal several times a day, several resuscitations, many infections, anaemia and non-functioning bowels. Her fragile skin bled when touched, she was ventilated for four weeks and unable to tolerate EBM for four weeks. She required eight blood transfusions and phototherapy, suffered from bradycardia and apnoeas and was administered caffeine to stimulate her brain. Her prognosis was uncertain for quite some time.

My expectations of motherhood had been shattered. I had lost 14 weeks of my pregnancy and was unable to perform the most basic task of motherhood: to hold my precious baby. The only care function that I could execute unaided for her was to express milk every three hours. Even that task had to be completed by the nursing staff who tube-fed my daughter for

10 weeks. We spent every waking hour at her incubator. We were rewarded by Mother Nature after two weeks as we witnessed her fused eyelids open and she viewed the world that had been transmitting sounds to her tiny brain. One of my cherished memories is that we were the first people that our daughter saw as she opened her eyes to this world. After three weeks I was allowed to hold my daughter, and, despite the alarms, machines and tubes, it was my first proper experience of motherhood.

Amelia went on to contract MRSA and required isolation and barrier nursing. Little did we realise but the friendships formed with other parents whose children were in the NICU at the same time as Amelia would become an integral part of our lives in the years to come. For a further six weeks, Amelia remained on CPAP. Finally, after several steps backwards, many nights of watching her fragile life hover on the precipice of life and death, she progressed to breathing unaided – a goal that even amazed the medical team who had expected her to be discharged home on oxygen. Seven weeks into Amelia's hospital stay her consultant offered us the first glimmer of hope that our daughter was going to survive her early arrival – the nights of frantic terror and heartache wondering if Amelia would see the dawn negated at last. Amelia was discharged home on Christmas Eve 2006 and remained on an MR10 apnoea monitor for five months. Feeding difficulties, reflux, endless hospital appointments, apnoeas, RSV, worrying about illness and developmental issues became the norm in the subsequent months. The unnatural, surreal and oftentimes frantic world of the NICU for all its faults had provided us with a comfort, reassurance and normality which wasn't available in the home environment.

Amelia has undergone physiotherapy, occupational therapy and speech therapy. She continues to suffer from CLD as a result of not receiving steroid injections prior to her birth. She developed a haemangioma on her left foot, which has left her foot misshapen and discoloured. Consequently, she has lost toenails and has an increased tendency to bleed. Her limbs are still hypertonic, and her balance is compromised by her prematurity. Despite this, she functions as a normal happy five-year-old little girl who loves ballet, singing and playing princesses. Every milestone she reaches is one step further from the NICU, her battle to survive against the odds and the heartache and pain of our introduction to parenthood. Every day that Amelia shares with us is a cherished memory and serves to push the early painful memories of her birth further into the recesses of our minds.

Premature birth has a profound effect on the family unit, but, thanks to the tireless efforts of the medical team who challenged the boundaries of medical science for our daughter, we have grown in strength as a family, learnt about the fragility and preciousness of life and managed to overcome the challenges that Mother Nature put our way.

Photographs of Amelia McDermott.

Amelia, two days old

Week 1, Amelia holding on to Mum's finger for dear life

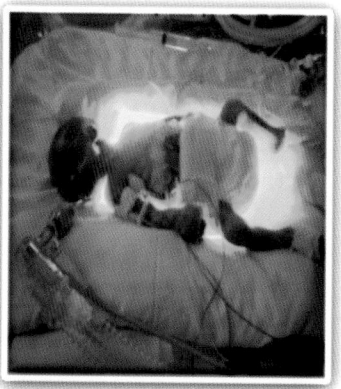

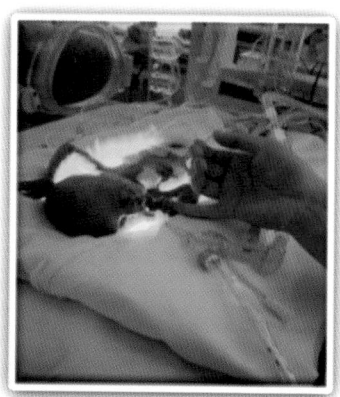

Amelia, two days home from hospital, 12 weeks old

Amelia, aged four

Aoife Ni Chonghaile (31 weeks) and Meabh Ni Chonghaile (27 weeks)

Our daughter Meabh's story began on 14 January when, due to PET, she had to be delivered by emergency Caesarean section at 27 weeks' gestation. She weighed a tiny 0.61 kg (1 lb 5 oz), and little did we know of the journey that lay ahead. We were asked to think about christening Meabh as she was very unwell and required the total support of a ventilator. She had some very bad days where the doctors did not expect her to pull through. Meabh had two bleeds to her brain: a grade-3 bleed and a grade-4 bleed. We were told that she would have severe disabilities and were asked to think about why we were keeping her alive on a ventilator.

It was so hard to leave her at night-time, as there is no parent accommodation available in the hospital. I would wake up the next day and rush to the hospital not knowing if Meabh was going to have a good or bad day. There were times when her chances of survival dropped to 30 per cent, namely when she was treated for a PDA.

When Meabh was three weeks old, we got to hold her for the first time. It was both an exciting and a scary moment as she was so tiny and covered in tubes. Later the nursing staff recommended we try kangaroo care, and I can't describe what an amazing feeling it was. Both Meabh's daddy and I proceeded to do kangaroo care regularly after that, which really helped us all.

Finally, having been ventilated for 49 days, Meabh was moved to CPAP. This was an amazing ray of hope for us; what a fighter our little girl was turning out to be. Meabh stayed on CPAP for another two months, and during this time she was transferred back to intensive care twice. We often felt like it was one step forward and two steps back. For a couple of hours a day she would use oxygen prongs to enable us to bottle-feed her and work on improving her sucking reflex. It was a long and difficult road, as she aspirated several times and had to go on BiPAP and once ended up back in intensive care. Eventually the doctors put Meabh on courses of steroids to try to wean her off the oxygen. During this time, Meabh developed ROP and had to have laser treatment on both eyes.

At four months we were told that Meabh would probably need a tracheotomy to prevent the aspirations. At that point we had been transferred to a hospital nearer home. Meabh had a feeding tube put in to her duodenum to reduce the occurrence of aspirations.

Meabh started to thrive, and on 14 September we were finally able to bring her home from hospital (on nasal oxygen). It had been eight tough months, but we eventually got our little girl home. Three days later, Meabh's lungs collapsed again, and it was decided that she needed to get a PEG in her tummy for feeding, as she was constantly aspirating. Meabh spent nearly two years on oxygen, and it actually seemed like home was a mini-hospital. The amount of equipment we had at home frightened some people, but we were so used to it all. We had an oxygen machine, cylinders of oxygen for the car and under the buggy, saturation monitors and a breathing monitor for under Meabh's mattress, a kangaroo pump and a medicine cupboard for all her medications.

The first three years of her life were taken up with hospital check-ups and admissions, some of which were close calls. Meabh is now six years old. She has not required oxygen in nearly three years and is getting her PEG removed next month. She has passed all her milestones and has amazed everyone who reads her medical notes. Meabh is still closely monitored due to her history of brain bleeds, but amazingly she is still showing no sign of any disabilities. Meabh is very short-sighted in her right eye, wears glasses and is closely monitored with eye tests every couple of months. She is entering her second year of mainstream school and is fluent in both English and Irish.

Meabh has a little sister, Aoife, who was also prematurely born at 31 weeks, weighing 1.22 kg (2 lb 11 oz). We find it so amazing the difference between being born at 27 weeks and at 31 weeks. Thankfully Aoife had no complications and was allowed home after five weeks. Meabh now shows Aoife pictures of when they were both born and in hospital in their incubators. To our girls this is normal, something they have in common, but to us it just shows that they are miracles.

Photographs of Aoife Ni Chonghaile and Meabh Ni Chonghaile.

Meabh, just one week old   *Meabh on CPAP, holding on*

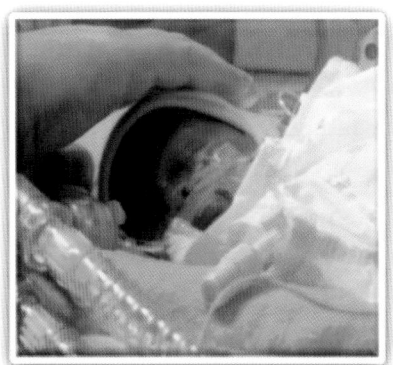 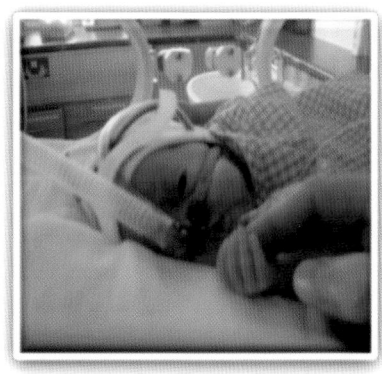

Meabh and Aoife playing together   *Meabh's first day at school*

Ava Bambury (31 weeks)

Ava's story began long before she was even conceived. We had suffered multiple miscarriages prior to having her so were over the moon when we finally saw a heartbeat on our fifth pregnancy. We thought all our bad luck was behind us and began to look forward to the next nine months. The first few months were uneventful apart from a few small bleeds, and at week 26 I was admitted for a bleed and was given steroids in case I had to deliver. It was at this stage that the hospital noticed that the baby wasn't growing as she should, and I was told to prepare for delivery the following week. We were devastated as she was only the size of a 24- or 25-week baby, but thankfully by the following week there had been a little growth so they decided to hold off delivery. I spent the next few weeks in hospital until she had completely stopped growing at 31 weeks and the decision was made to deliver her immediately.

Ava was born on 2 June weighing 1.5 kg (3 lb 7 oz). To this day I still can't believe I have the little girl I have always wanted, and I still get very emotional just thinking about it.

As soon as Ava was born she was rushed to the NICU where she spent the next few weeks overcoming the usual problems that premature babies encounter: she needed help to breathe, a tube to feed her and caffeine to keep her alert. She also had numerous IV lines to deliver medication and required UV-light therapy as she was suffering from jaundice. Ava had a large PDA, which is a heart problem common in premature babies, and she also had some congenital heart defects, a PFO and an atrial septal defect, which thankfully have not required surgery. She was also diagnosed with preauricular tag, which was removed in a small operation when she was 11 months old, and a sacral dimple. I expressed breastmilk for Ava for three months, which I found tough going. Ava had bad reflux, and it seemed like I was always feeding or expressing; however, I really feel this benefited Ava and helped her immune system to develop.

We took Ava home after a month, weighing just 1.7 kg (3 lb 15 oz), and our house went into lockdown. We used more hand soap and sanitiser than we had ever used before. We had the cleanest house in Kildare, and we decided that no visitors, except grandparents, were allowed to visit us for the first few weeks. Whilst most people dress their babies up to go visiting or shopping, our only outings were hospital visits, where I dressed my little lady up for the other mammies in the waiting room. Things began to settle down, and I returned to work when Ava was 10 months old. Then, at a routine appointment, cerebral palsy was mentioned, and two weeks later, at 11 months of age, Ava was officially diagnosed with spastic diplegia cerebral palsy.

Our whole world came crashing down. We were devastated as the doctors didn't know if she would ever walk by herself. Miraculously, over the next year, thanks to the team in Enable Ireland and lots of home physiotherapy, Ava began to walk and can now even run. Ava has had many appointments over the past two years, and at times it has been very difficult, but I feel very lucky to have received carer's benefit which allowed me to take two months off work when Ava started Enable Ireland. We still enjoy meeting up with other premature babies, and although Irish Premature Babies was not set up when I had Ava, I have no doubt their support would have been invaluable.

Ava continues to have many appointments and lots of physiotherapy, and she is still under the care of the hospital where she was born. Ava is under investigation for failure to thrive (a problem common in IUGR babies) and short stature, but we are confident that she will overcome these issues and any more that she may encounter. Ava's determination and fighting spirit have astounded everyone who meets her, and she is a very different girl in real life than her medical records show. We couldn't have hoped for anything more. She is the happiest little girl we know. Unfortunately, the type of growth restriction that Ava suffered would most likely return in future pregnancies, and, given our history, another even more premature baby would be expected. For now we are just so grateful to have our little miracle running around and getting up to mischief as every toddler her age should be.

Photographs of Ava Bambury.

Ava when she was five days old

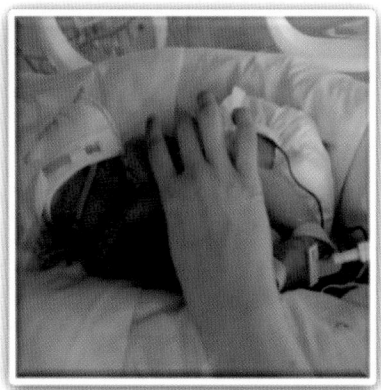

Ava at six weeks old

Ava on her first birthday

Ava with Mam and Dada

Ava Caslin (31 weeks)

Ava was born at 31 weeks and 4 days' gestation. As my first baby arrived at 37 weeks, I had no reason to expect anything other than a similar outcome on my second pregnancy. The pregnancy progressed well up to week 25 when I was diagnosed with elevated blood pressure and protein in my urine. I continued to be monitored as an outpatient at the hospital until Friday, 12 November, when my condition worsened and my GP referred me immediately to the hospital.

Upon arrival I was given the steroid injections to develop my baby's lungs. Whilst waiting to receive the second steroid injection, a scan was carried out that indicated that the baby had not grown since the 29-week scan. I was admitted to hospital at that stage. Two days later, the midwife informed me that I needed to fast as there was a possibility of my baby being delivered that day. A further scan was ordered in which the baby's heartbeat was noted to be dropping. She was unconscious and still hadn't grown. The staff immediately contacted the neonatal transport team as they feared the baby would need high-level intensive care in Dublin. I just about had time to contact my partner Brendan and my mum to inform them of the impending delivery. My mother present in the theatre with me, and at 3.20 p.m., my daughter Ava was born. All the medical team present laughed when they heard Ava crying as she entered the world. As a nurse later explained, it was assumed that Ava would be too ill to cry so they were amazed and delighted to hear her announce her own arrival. She was taken immediately to the SCBU.

I was eventually allowed up to see her at 11.00 p.m. that night, although some medical staff were reluctant due to the late hour. However, my protestations that she was my baby and that I needed to see her soon won them over. She looked so tiny, so vulnerable. She was only 1.5 kg (3 lb 5 oz). She had lanugo (fine hair) covering her entire body. She didn't have any fingernails, eyelashes or eyebrows. I just stood looking at her in shock, wondering if this little baby would survive.

The following morning, I went to visit her at 7.00 a.m. only to discover that her cot was empty. I burst into tears and immediately assumed the worst – that she had passed away in the night. Thankfully the staff were on hand to assure me that my little miracle was stable and had only been moved into an incubator. The consultant from the SCBU was wonderful; he sat down with us and explained in detail what was ahead of us on our journey with our premature baby. They proposed to commence feeds the next day, but we were fully informed about possible issues that might ensue as a result of this action.

The next day, as expected, Ava was very jaundiced and had to have phototherapy. They discovered she had an infection in her stomach, and she was taken off feeds and put on antibiotics. I maintained the three-hourly expressing regime to ensure sufficient supplies of milk for when feeds recommenced.

Exactly one week after Ava was born I finally got to hold my precious baby, an occasion tinged with excitement and sheer terror. As I was only permitted to cuddle Ava once each day, I made sure that each cuddle became a cherished moment for us. Because Ava kept pulling out her feeding tube, the medical staff decided to try to feed her independently with a bottle, a task that required quite a bit of perseverance and coaxing, but, like all these precious fighters, Ava mastered it in the end.

On 6 December we were informed that Ava was well enough to come home with us, much to our relief, as due to adverse weather the daily trip to the hospital was taking us

Tiny Footprints

four hours. Initially it was nerve-wracking to bring a 2.72 kg (4 lb) baby home out of the security of the SCBU, but we settled into our home routine pretty quickly.

Ava is nine months now. She is doing well although she is still very small and is due to be referred to a dietician soon. She still attends her development checks as well as her eye and hearing appointments. She has an allergy to milk, and the left side of her body is a little weaker. She is our precious miracle who makes our family complete in every way.

Photographs of Ava Caslin.

Ava, one hour old

Ava, five days old

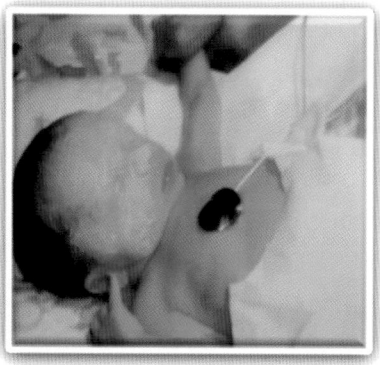

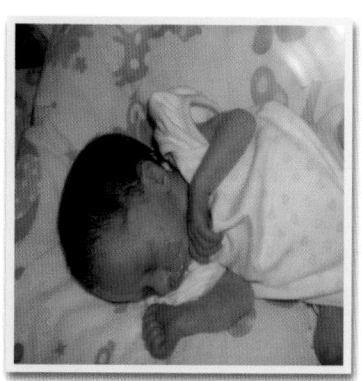

Ava with her big sister Aimee at five months

Ava now

ભ

Ava Grace Dempsey (28 weeks)

On 22 January our lives changed for ever. Our beautiful daughter Ava Grace entered the world more than 12 weeks early, weighing 1.11 kg (2 lb 7 oz) at the Rotunda Hospital, Dublin. She was whipped away so quickly that at first we didn't even know if she was a boy or a girl. The medical team got to work on her straight away, and she was brought straight up to the NICU. It was the next day before I got to see her due to complications of my own, but that day her daddy Paul went to see her, and word was she was doing quite well. That night I lay in bed with a picture of my tiny daughter in my hands.

The next day I finally got to see her. Paul and I cried as we looked in at our fragile little girl with tubes and wires attached to her tiny little body. Later, when we returned with my mam, the doctor informed us that Ava had a grade-4 bleed on her brain. He told us this was the worst grade of bleed and would usually lead to developmental problems and disability, but to what level he did not know. It was really down to the individual baby, but it wasn't looking good. Also, a duct in Ava's heart had not closed and would require treatment and possibly surgery if the medication didn't work. Our world fell apart. We were left completely devastated and felt utterly hopeless.

We asked that members of our family stay away as we were too upset to see them. Thankfully, close family and friends still came to see us at the hospital, and in hindsight this was exactly what we needed. It was this support that helped us through the most difficult time of our lives. Every day we sat by Ava's incubator willing her on with everything we had. The rest of our family and friends rallied round, and everyone we knew prayed for our baby girl.

There were many ups and downs along the way. Ava needed numerous blood transfusions and two courses of treatment which failed to close the duct in her heart. It was decided to hold off on surgery to see if the duct would close itself. Thankfully, she didn't need laser treatment on her eyes like many other premature babies, one blessing to be thankful for. Every day, Paul and I would both give our daughter kangaroo care and chat to her about all her family that she had yet to meet. I continued to express milk, the one practical thing I could do for her that would help to bring her on.

It was five weeks later when Ava's brain scan showed that the bleed appeared to be resolving, which was very unusual for a bleed of this magnitude. Paul's parents were present while the doctor scanned Ava's brain, and it was Paul's mother Klena who rang me with this unbelievable news. I thought she must be mistaken as we were told this couldn't possibly happen. I just couldn't take it in. When I arrived at the hospital the doctor confirmed it. We will never forget hearing the news: it was without doubt the best moment of our lives. That same week, the duct in Ava's heart closed. Things were really starting to look up.

Over the next few weeks we watched Ava getting stronger. She improved on her feeds, came off CPAP, moved into a cot and got to wear her own clothes. She started to look like a real newborn. It was finally time to come home, but there was one last brain scan to recheck the status of the bleed and also to assess for other abnormalities. As the doctor scanned Ava's brain, I begged my dad to help her from up above, and when Ava got the all clear the nurses were so happy for us, whooping and hugging us. It was a very happy moment.

Ava left the hospital weighing 2.47 kg (5 lb 7 oz), and as we put her in her car seat, her face broke out in a beaming smile. It was as if she knew she was finally coming home. Since that day Ava has really thrived. She attended physiotherapy for 18 months as a precaution to ensure there were no lasting effects from the bleed, and today Ava is a very happy, clever little girl who idolises Barney. Thankfully, she has reached all her milestones. She has such a zest for life and embraces everything with such enthusiasm. She has a very independent streak and always says, 'I'll do it myself.' We are truly blessed with our amazing daughter. We remember vividly the anguish and pain we suffered during that time and through our story would like to give hope to others who are going through this difficult process. Never give up hope: miracles really can happen.

Photographs of Ava Grace Dempsey.

Ava Grace, one day old

Ava Grace, three weeks old

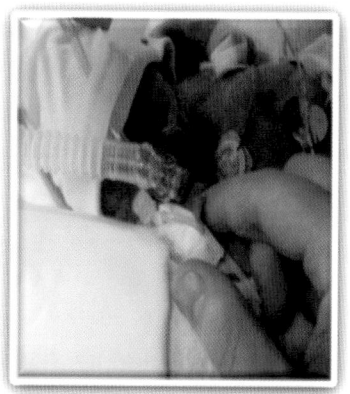

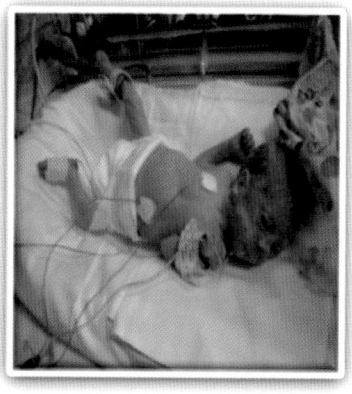

Ava Grace, 21 months old

Ava Grace, two years and four months

Ava Lewis (29 weeks)

On Saturday, 27 March, our little girl Ava Madeleine Lewis made a dramatic entrance into the world almost 11 weeks early. That day we had planned a shopping trip to buy nursery bits and pieces, presuming we were very well prepared for our June baby. However, Ava had other ideas.

Despite a pretty easy and comfortable pregnancy, I had felt strange for a couple of days previous, and my active and wriggly bump had seemed quiet, almost tired. Following a restless night of worry, we decided to ring the hospital at first light and were advised to come in straight away. The next couple of hours passed by in a blur of questions, cardiotocography traces and ultrasound sonography scans culminating in an emergency Caesarean section due to oligohydramnios. We were now the proud but completely shocked parents of the most beautiful little girl we had ever laid eyes on.

Ava, who weighed just 0.98 kg (2 lb 1 oz), was immediately whisked away in what resembled a small sandwich bag, to the NICU. As the medical personnel took her away, all we could see was her tiny little head with these huge eyes staring at us. Later that night, when we finally got to meet our daughter properly, her face was masked by UV goggles and breathing apparatus. Her body was covered with wires and tubes. We cried and fretted and longed to see her tiny face again. In the very early hours, amidst a blur of expressing milk and tears, I wandered to the NICU, where I got to cuddle our little girl for the first time with the help of the amazing staff. They immediately emailed a picture to Ava's daddy: she was his absolute double.

The first two weeks of her life were a roller-coaster of highs and lows. Incredibly, she never required ventilation and was just cycled on CPAP for a few days. We couldn't believe our luck, but events soon took a turn for the worse. Ava's abdomen became distended, and she was unable to tolerate even a millilitre of EBM. Our worst fears were confirmed: she had suspected NEC. All feeds were held, and she was treated with antibiotics for seven days. This seemed like an eternity as we knew the longer she wasn't feeding the longer it would be until we got her home.

Eventually, after stopping and starting for 15 days, she was finally able to tolerate her tube-feeds again, each day taking a little bit more. However, a blood infection and anaemia stopped us in our tracks as she required a further course of antibiotics and numerous transfusions. We were so emotional, so scared and felt so isolated, and all we could do was wait.

The NICU seemed like another world; it was as if nothing existed outside of the NICU doors. The one thing that helped us was talking to the other parents in the NICU, and we soon realised that the ultimate gift we could give our little fighter was our patience.

Day 21 was momentous. Ava was infection-free and feeding well enough to graduate to NICU2. We were absolutely over the moon, as we saw our tiny little mite grow stronger and stronger. From the beginning, her determination shone through, and she was affectionately known as 'Screamer'. She regularly 'escaped' from her incubator nest to the bottom corner of her incubator, a trick she continues to this day in her cot.

The early days of Ava's life were so tough; every time we left the hospital and our baby our hearts ached, and it seemed like we were missing something . . . a piece of ourselves. The house seemed so empty even though she had never lived there. As each day passed, we all got a little braver, and on day 38 Ava moved to special care. The next few days were amazing, finally getting to dress and cuddle our baby properly without the fear of breaking her tiny body. We worked hard to wean her off tube-feeds and bottles, and with the support and encouragement of the lactation nurses and NICU staff we progressed to fully breastfeeding. She was nearly ready for home. On day 47 the home-liaison nurse asked us if we had our car seat ready, as tomorrow was the big day. On 14 May, weighing 1.62 kg (3 lb 9 oz), we took our Polly Pocket home.

She is now a happy, healthy, incredibly determined and mischievous toddler, our little miracle, small but mighty, and we are so proud of her and grateful to everyone who helped us along the way.

Photographs of Ava Lewis.

Ava, just four days old

Ava having a little chew, at 21 days old

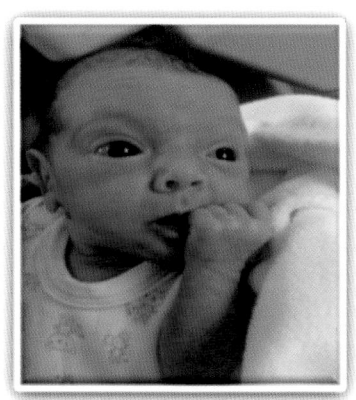

Ava at eight months

Ava playing away at 12 months

Ben Curran Merrigan (25 weeks)

On 11 October, Ben was born in the NMH, Holles Street, Dublin, by emergency Caesarean section due to pre-eclampsia. He was born at 25 weeks, weighing 0.45 kg (1 lb). Due to his low weight we weren't given much hope for Ben. We were told if he is pink and cries they would do everything for him, but if not there wasn't much they could do. Our little angel came out pink and filled the room with his cry.

I didn't get to see Ben when he was born, but his dad met him for a brief second before he was rushed to the NICU. Ben had a lot of challenges ahead of him. It was two days before I met my little angel. Going into the NICU was such a terrifying experience. I didn't know what to expect.

By day 3, Ben's weight had dropped to 0.39 kg (13 oz). He was so small and fragile, I was afraid to even touch him. His skin was so thin you could see right through it. We always tried to be brave and smile and stay positive for Ben. He was three weeks old the first time I held him. When the nurse suggested kangaroo care, I was so excited yet terrified. I was afraid to move in the chair with all the cables and tubes attached to Ben, but it was such an amazing feeling holding him for the first time and having skin-to-skin contact. I craved for mother-and-baby bonding time and jumped at every opportunity I got to hold him.

While in the NICU Ben had a lot of ups and downs. On more than one occasion, we thought we could lose him, but from day 1 he was a fighter. While Ben was in the NMH he had a PDA and was treated for NEC three times. He had jaundice, two hernia operations, CLD, stage-3 ROP (for which he had laser eye surgery), over 20 blood transfusions and several platelet transfusions.

Ben finally came home on 10 February after four long months in Holles Street. He was doing great at home, and we loved being a family at last. Then one night, while feeding Ben, he stopped breathing and we had to perform CPR. This was the most frightening experience of my entire life. In hospital they thought he had swallowed his milk wrong, and after two days we were discharged. The next day, Ben stopped breathing again, and we had to perform CPR yet again. Ben was admitted to intensive care in Our Lady's Children's Hospital, Crumlin. While in Crumlin Ben underwent a third hernia operation. However, after the operation Ben kept going into cardiac arrest, and the doctors didn't know why. Ben had a microlaryngoscopy and bronchoscopy which revealed he had a condition called tracheobroncomalsia (floppy windpipe). The only option for Ben was to get a tracheotomy, and he was ventilation-dependent.

After Ben got his trachy I was so scared to hold him, and it was like going back to when he was first born. I was afraid the tube would come out of his neck, but eventually we got used to it. The hardest part was not being able to hear him cry, laugh or make any sound. I hated to see him upset as it would upset me looking at him crying and not hearing any sound. Ben made it so easy for us. He was just a normal baby, and he was always so happy and did everything a normal baby does. The only difference was he had a tube in his neck and was connected to a machine to help him breathe. We spent 10 months in Crumlin after Ben got his tracheotomy. During this time, both myself and Ben's dad were trained in how to care for Ben at home. Ben was discharged from Our Lady's on 1 January – it was the best start to the New Year.

Ben is now 21 months old. He still has his tracheotomy but is no longer ventilation-dependent. He spent a total of 14 months in hospital. He cannot talk due to the trachy, so we are teaching him sign language. We are hopeful that he will get his trachy removed in the next couple of months, and I cannot wait to hear my little boy laugh. Ben is such a happy baby; he always has a smile on his face, and you would never know by looking at him what a tough start in life he endured. He is the light of both his dad's and my lives, and we are so proud to be his parents.

Photographs of Ben Curran Merrigan.

Ben, born at 25 weeks, at 0.45 kg

Papa Smurf loved dressing up in his cardigans knitted by his nanny

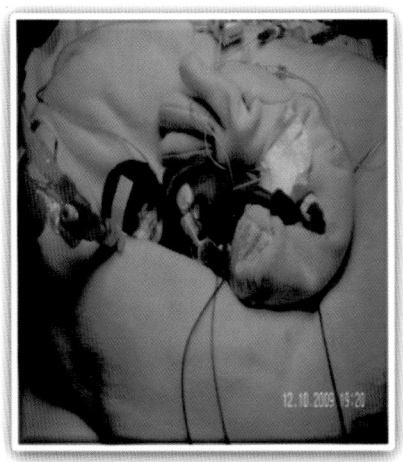

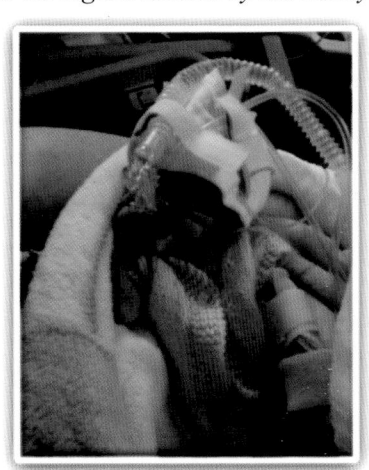

Ben at ten months, full of smiles

Ben

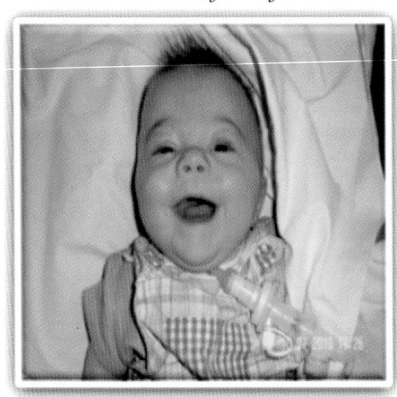

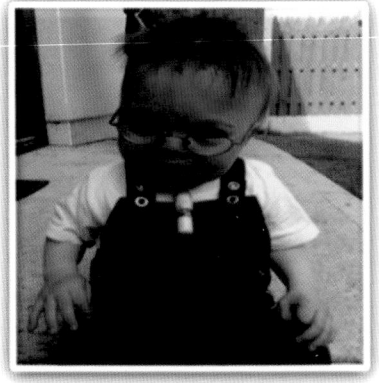

Brody Swayne Bradley (27 weeks)

We got a first black-and-white glimpse of Brody at our 12-week scan. Brody was measuring a few days ahead of dates. At 27 weeks the consultant told us that he was measuring as a 25-week gestation and the amniotic fluid level was low. As a precaution, I received the first steroid injection to help Brody's lungs. When we returned to the hospital for the second injection, an hour of tracing revealed that Brody was not moving and I was admitted to hospital. Whilst being scanned by the consultant the following morning he informed us that the blood flow from the placenta wasn't continuous and I would have to be transferred to a hospital with a neonatal ward. I didn't stop crying from the time the consultant said those words until I reached the other hospital an hour's drive away. Upon arrival I was scanned by a doctor, and Brody's movements were to be traced a few times a day. Even though the blood flow wasn't continuous it was still working, and as long as it didn't reverse the consultant was happy not to deliver him.

As the consultant scanned me the following morning she looked pleased. The amniotic fluid levels had increased and Brody was moving. As I smiled, looking at the screen, the blood flow came across, but it was reversed. I was told Brody would have to be delivered that day and my heart sank. I went back to my bed and two nurses were waiting. Within minutes I was gowned and ready. The walk to surgery was the most terrifying walk of my life. A million questions were in my head, but my mouth wouldn't open to ask any of them. Within minutes the room was full with people, doctors, the medical team and me waiting for Brody to be delivered. At 27 weeks and 6 days, on 28 November at 14.06 p.m., Brody was born by emergency Caesarean section. He weighed just 0.72 kg (1 lb 10 oz). I was told he wouldn't cry as his lungs were too small, but I heard a little weak cry. As Brody was being transferred to the NICU his incubator was wheeled over to my bed but I was unable to see him.

After five hours he was taken off the ventilator and put onto CPAP. I can still remember so clearly the noise of the machines beeping in NICU. Lying there so peaceful and still I couldn't believe how small he was, but he was perfect. When a baby kicks you have images of a big foot, but Brody's foot was the size of the top of my finger. He had so many different tubes and machines hooked up to him. His weight dropped to 0.67 kg (1 lb 8 oz). He started taking breastmilk, but only 1.2 ml every two hours.

After the results of his first brain scan came back normal, the doctor compared having a premature baby to a roller-coaster ride. We would have our good days and our bad days, and we would have to prepare ourselves for what was to come. During the first week we never touched our baby as I thought we weren't allowed – a bizarre thought admittedly, but this was our first baby in NICU. We asked for permission to take a picture, and the doctor laughed and told us that Brody was our baby. I couldn't wait to finally touch him, and after 21 days I got to hold my tiny baby.

Brody was on CPAP for 33 days and had nasal prongs for 10 days. He spent 50 days in Dublin before he was transferred to the local SCBU. After 68 days in hospital our little miracle came home, weighing 2.21 kg (4 lb 14 oz). By Brody's due date he had undergone four brain scans, an echocardiogram on his heart and regular eye examinations. We were so relieved that the brain scans and heart echo revealed no abnormalities. Brody has stage 2 ROP. The doctor told us that as long as the development of the eye stays ahead of the condition it might correct itself.

Brody is now a happy healthy little boy and has come a long way. When Brody was born one of the nurses said to me, 'Let Brody show you what he can do,' and she was right. When you experience the fighting spirit of these tiny miracles you realise how strong they really are. We have been extremely lucky with Brody, but ultimately he is the real hero of this story. He fought from the beginning, and we are so proud of him.

Photographs of Brody Swayne Bradley.

Brody, just three hours old

Brody, four days old

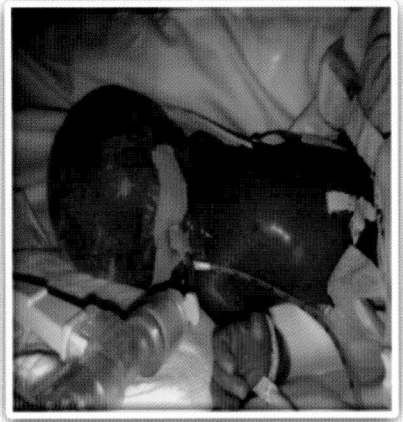
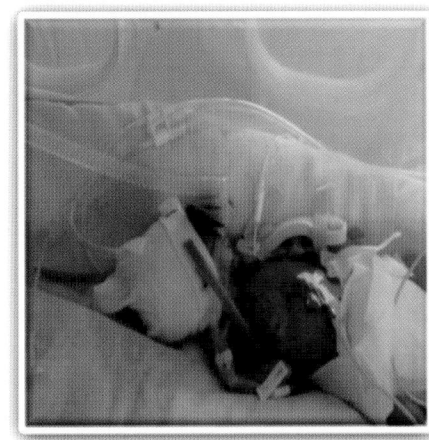

Brody at five weeks old

Brody at two months corrected

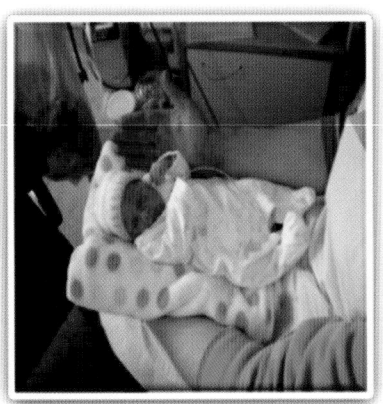
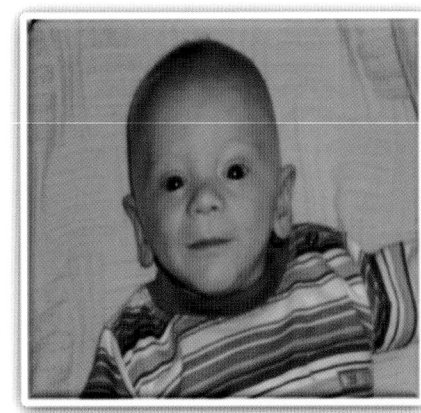

Cameron Hearn Phipps (25 weeks)

Six weeks after we had suffered a miscarriage on my fourth child, we were very surprised to find out I was due another baby. It was so scary, but after the scans everything seemed to be OK. At 25 weeks that changed, and I was rushed into hospital as I was going into early labour. Luckily, after a long hospital stay and a cocktail of drugs, they managed to stop the labour. Then, on 4 November, the date our lost baby was due to be born, I went into labour again. This time it was different though. When I got to the hospital they were all rushing around prepping me for surgery. I really didn't know what was going on. I was alone and terrified.

Our beautiful miracle Cameron was born, weighing 1.3 kg (2 lb 14 oz). Over the next few hours his condition dramatically deteriorated, and they had to transfer him. Luckily, they could send him immediately to the NMH. It all happened so quickly. My poor defenceless little man was wheeled into me in his incubator before going all the way to Dublin without me. I had to stay in Cavan General Hospital as I had a section so couldn't go with him straight away. Fortunately I was also transferred the next day. However, I was put in the normal post-natal ward with all the mammies and their new healthy babies while my little man was all alone in the NICU. Not that I was able to sleep anyway, but a nurse rushed into me during the night telling me that Cameron needed an emergency blood transfusion and that I needed to give them permission.

The following morning they gave him an ultrasound on his head where they discovered he had grade 3 and 4 brain haemorrhages. This was shocking enough, but then we were told his chances of survival were bleak. To be honest, everything after that was almost a blur. Cameron was on high ventilation, and the machine shook his tiny little body with every breath. It was horrible to watch, and he also had to be kept on morphine constantly. We didn't think things could get any worse, and then his lungs collapsed. We were told he would need an operation on his heart 'if he pulled through'. We never gave up on Cameron. The doctors may have been preparing us for the worst but we couldn't accept that. We had to believe we would get to take our little miracle home. I never gave up that hope. Inside I felt as if I was dying. The pain and guilt I felt cannot be put into words. My heart hurt so much. It's a mother's first instinct to protect her child, and I couldn't do that. It was in the doctors' hands, but I felt so guilty.

Over the next few weeks Cameron gradually started to improve. It was such a relief when they took him off the shaky ventilator, but he was still on high ventilation. Then I got the moment I missed out on after he was born, the most memorable and happy day I had in a long time. They let me hold him. I couldn't believe it. It was the best feeling in the world to be able to hold his skin against mine, smell his baby smell and feel his tiny heartbeat. It was amazing, but it was also a little scary. I just didn't want the moment to end. The next day we were told he was finally going to be given some of the expressed milk I had stored for him. I was delighted that something I did was going to help him, but that didn't go according to plan. Cameron developed NEC.

However, Cameron got stronger and stronger, and when the time came for him to go on assisted breathing he was only on it for a few days. The doctors didn't have a very promising prognosis for him though. They didn't think he would ever be able to suck a bottle, or walk or talk or smile. No parent ever wants to hear that, but we never accepted any of that, and we knew after all the hard work Cameron had put in he wasn't going to stop there. He was going to prove them all wrong.

Tiny Footprints

Cameron was discharged the day before Christmas Eve, just in time for Santa. He was on different medications and special formula, but each day he got bigger and bigger. Everyone who meets Cameron always comments on his smile. He is the happiest little boy, running around after his brother and sisters. He is with Enable Ireland now for therapy, but he has made his mammy and daddy so proud.

Photographs of Cameron Hearn Phipps.

Cameron, born 11 weeks early

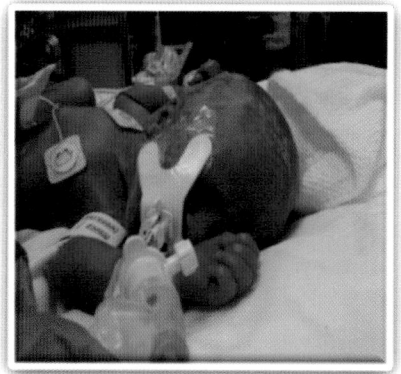

Cameron with Mammy at four weeks

Cameron at five weeks old

Yay! Cameron at 21 months

Caoimhe Dunne (25 weeks)

It was with a routine 24-week check-up with my GP that my story begins. I felt fine; little did I know my blood pressure was very elevated and there was protein in my urine. I was referred to hospital where I was taken straight to the HDU in the delivery suite. There was a flurry of activity, where a team of specialists worked frantically, inserting IV lines for medicines into my arms. I was connected to all sorts of monitors and a catheter bag. In the midst of all that activity, an obstetrician was doing an ultrasound scan. Strangely enough I felt fine apart from the shock that was quickly setting in due to the frenzy.

I was told I had severe pre-eclampsia, and that if I didn't start to respond to the drugs they would have no choice but to deliver the baby as my life was at risk. I was stunned. How could I be so ill and yet feel so fine? I couldn't believe what was happening. A NICU paediatrician came to see me that night to explain the complications a baby would most likely suffer if delivered this early. Exactly what she said is all a bit of a blur. I zoned out after she mentioned brain bleeds, cerebral palsy, blindness, ventilators; I was numb.

My liver, kidneys and blood were being affected as the PET had developed into HELLP Syndrome. So, on Sunday, 21 September, at 12.15 p.m., my tiny warrior Caoimhe was delivered at 25 weeks by Caesarean section, weighing 0.57 kg (1 lb 4 oz). She was resuscitated and whisked off to the NICU, stopping briefly for me to see her from the operating table.

I didn't see her again for three days. I saw a photo on my husband's mobile that made her look gigantic, but I didn't realise how small she was until I saw her for myself – a moment that will forever be a heart-wrenching memory for me. I nearly got sick when I saw the tiny creature that was my baby. My whole body started to tremble. She was on a ventilator and covered from head to toe with wires and tubes and plasters. She had a black eye mask on to protect her eyes from the phototherapy light that she was under for jaundice. I can't describe what she looked like, I just remember thinking, *there is no way that 'this' is going to survive.* I couldn't even comprehend that 'this' was a baby. She looked like a test-tube alien toy that my nephew had. She was almost transparent, her skin wrinkled, hairy and bruised-looking, and she was literally just skin and bone. I was totally devastated, and I couldn't speak to anyone. All I could do was cry, and that continued for the horrendous weeks that followed while I felt I was just waiting, waiting for the bad news to come.

Caoimhe had one problem after another. We got a premature baby book, and she had almost every problem in it. She had RDS and all that goes with it. Being ventilated for so long she developed CLD. She had a PDA of the heart, sepsis, a pulmonary haemorrhage and so many blood transfusions that I stopped counting. She spent a further eight weeks on CPAP and then went onto prongs for three weeks before finally coming off all oxygen on St Stephen's Day. It was amazing to see her little face at last with nothing stuck to it. The next challenge was getting her to take a bottle-feed. She would stop breathing and turn a blue and grey colour – a very scary sight to behold. We eventually took her home on 6 January, weighing 3.23 kg (7 lb 2 oz), after 80 days in the NICU and 27 days in the SCBU.

For the first two years, when I checked on her I was checking to see 'if she was dead', but now I check on her to see if she's OK. She's almost three now and doing great. She has some minor problems and is slightly delayed developmentally, but nothing major. Not a single day goes by that I don't remember the hours staring like a zombie, bewildered, lost and broken into the incubator. Thankfully for us we got a 'happy ever after' ending, the stuff of fairy tales. Against all odds our little miracle made it home. It's changed me for ever, but I wouldn't change her for the world.

Photographs of Caoimhe Dunne.

Caoimhe at nine days old

Caoimhe at 16 days old

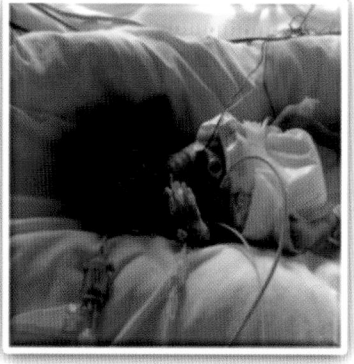

Caoimhe at 90 days old, her first Christmas spent in the NICU.

Caoimhe at two and a half years

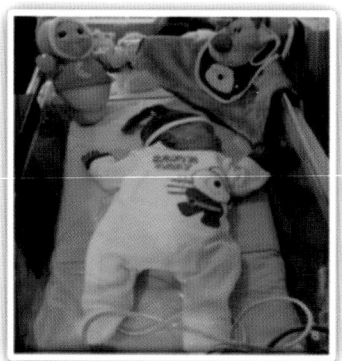

ℭ

Caolum Dyas (28 weeks)

When I was pregnant with my son I was admitted to Our Lady of Lourdes Hospital in Drogheda with pre-eclampsia. On the third day of observation I hadn't felt much movement and asked to be put on the monitor to ease my mind, as I was a little concerned. It was then noticed that the baby's heart rate was very weak. Within a few minutes the room was full with doctors and nurses who were very concerned about my baby. Immediately the decision was made to carry out an emergency Caesarean section.

Caolum was born on 6 August, at 28 weeks, weighing 0.98 kg (2 lb 2 oz), less than a bag of sugar, as he likes to say himself. So begins our story of life in the NICU. Caolum spent his first night in a turkey roasting bag in an effort to try and maintain his body temperature. He was also under lights to keep him warm and hooked up to numerous machines and monitors. Caolum spent his first 36 to 48 hours on the ventilator, which helped him to breathe, but the staff weaned him off it, allowing him to breathe on his own. The NICU became his (and our) home for the next 12 weeks. Here he spent most of that time on CPAP, fighting infections and receiving numerous blood transfusions.

The following weeks in the ICU were like a roller-coaster, with many ups and downs. Caolum had numerous blood tests, X-rays and brain scans. Due to his prematurity, Caolum would frequently stop breathing. This would in turn lead to his heart rate slowing way down, causing a drop in his blood pressure. The staff, and ourselves after a while, would stimulate Caolum by rubbing or patting him to get him to start breathing again. Once these episodes became more frequent, Caolum would be put back on CPAP to aid his breathing. He also had digestive issues, and on a few occasions had to be taken off milk for days and slowly reintroduced to it, starting with minute quantities, sometimes as little as 1 ml per hour.

After nine weeks Caolum was moved out of the incubator and into a cot in the nursery where he thrived for the next two weeks. He had eye tests to observe how they developed, and for the first few weeks the prognosis was good. But that changed. The day before we were to take him home, it was noticed that his eyes were no longer developing as normal, and an appointment was arranged with an eye specialist in Temple Street Children's University Hospital in Dublin. Despite the news about his eyes, Caolum was allowed home with us that day. The following morning, he had to attend an appointment in the eye clinic in Temple Street. It was discovered that he had the advancing stages of ROP. He was readmitted to hospital to rectify the retinopathy. He underwent laser surgery the next morning in the NMH in Dublin and spent the next few days under observation. Caolum left hospital exactly one week after his due date.

On reflection we feel very lucky that we live so close to the hospital so that we could and did spend as much time as possible with Caolum in NICU. At times we felt useless, unable to help him, but we were comforted and reassured when we gave Caolum kangaroo care on a number of occasions, which resulted in his vital signs stabilising. In addition, because Caolum was our first child, every minute of every day and every ounce of our energy went into Caolum and his fight in NICU.

Since leaving hospital, Caolum has had no setbacks. Temple Street continue to test his eyes periodically, and these appointments have become less frequent as he gets older. He is now a happy and healthy seven-year-old who attends and excels in mainstream school. He is a confident child and mixes well with other children. He is the older brother to Cian, who he idolises, who thankfully was born full term and is now two years old. But Caolum will always be our little miracle. 'Small in stature, big in heart.'

Photographs of Caolum Dyas.

Caolum, just one week old

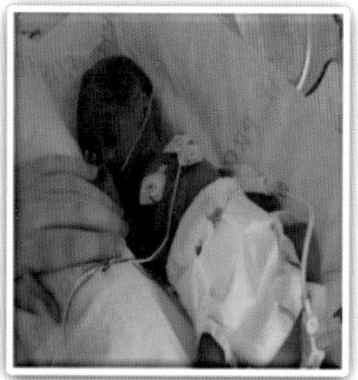

Caolum having cuddles

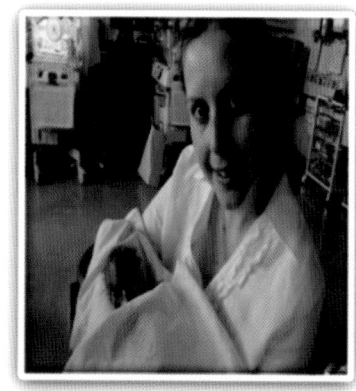

Caolum, age four

Caolum, age seven and big brother to Cian

Tiny Footprints

ଔ

Cillian Fegan (30 weeks)
and Oisín Fegan (31 weeks)

Did you ever get that gut feeling that things are not going the way you imagined? That's how I felt on my first viable pregnancy after miscarriages. Fourteen weeks of a threatened miscarriage and high blood pressure did nothing to alleviate that niggling feeling. At 28 weeks, birth looked imminent, but the baby held on somehow for another two weeks when a haemorrhage broke my waters, triggering labour. Cillian was a Caesarean birth after 20-odd hours in labour. At least I did not miss that joy. At 30 weeks' gestation, he needed to go into the NICU.

The first time I saw Cillian he was on assisted breathing with wires everywhere, he had shades on his eyes, was hairy with lanugo and had a nappy on up to his neck. He had the usual litany of premature issues: dropping heart rate, apnoea, jaundice, was a dreadful feeder and was not much more than skin and bone. Six weeks of life skills' learning and he received an honourable discharge.

At 13 weeks, our little man needed to have an inguinal hernia operated on. A couple of days after his release from hospital he became unwell, but A&E assured us that it was a virus that might get a little worse. However, less than 24 hours later, he was being resuscitated in A&E having contracted bacterial meningitis. We spent the most difficult six weeks of our lives in an isolation room at the hospital watching our baby being given many different types of drugs to kill this infection before it killed him. The medication caused his body and face to swell up, and he was so sick his skin was the same colour as a typical Irish day: grey. It was touch and go for a while, and we really didn't know if we were ever going to take him home. But this little guy had an inner fighting spirit, and he eventually came home baldy, battered and bruised, but he came home.

Symptomatic of Cillian's prematurity was that he had delayed visual maturation (a retinal development problem) and didn't see until he was eight months old. Eight months of not seeing our lovely faces, talk about bad luck. The combination of prematurity and meningitis necessitated Cillian having to attend speech therapy along with eye, audio and regular developmental clinics. At two years of age, we noticed him having seizures, which were subsequently diagnosed as epilepsy. Moreover, his behaviour with his peers saw us consult his paediatrician, who referred him on to a psychologist and occupational therapist. The resultant diagnosis was 'sensory processing disorder', a disorder that affects Cillian's spatial awareness of himself and the world around him. He is currently undergoing investigation for renal issues, and he just had an adenoidectomy.

Two years after the birth of Cillian, my husband and I decided to try for another baby, convincing ourselves I could have a 'normal' pregnancy. Within two days of the pregnancy confirmation, the bleeding started all over again, only now it was much worse. I knew in my heart and soul that my somewhat inhospitable and unfriendly womb was going to cause problems. At 30 weeks I was admitted to hospital with bleeding. One minute I was pretending to do a crossword on the bed, the next I was in theatre with a lovely man's hands around my neck trying to induce unconsciousness as quick as possible. I was then given a general anaesthetic. I had a placental abruption, which broke my waters, in turn causing my little footling breech baby to fall down with the cord around his foot, causing a cord prolapse. I know that without the staff in the Rotunda Hospital I would not have a second son. It was miles away from the type of birth I had envisaged.

So, if anybody is looking for scented candles, calming music and a birthing ball, just give me a shout, I have some never used at home.

I woke up in the HDU to the news that my new son Oisín was doing well in the NICU and that his daddy was with him. I got the pleasure of meeting him the next day. He was breathing on his own, despite the traumatic birth, which required resuscitations. He was black and blue and had a few war wounds from the knife. It felt like déjà-vu being in the same unit again, but it was strangely comforting knowing the staff and routine of the unit. Oisín passed basic training and came home at 34 weeks' gestation.

The two boys are brothers for sure, with the same eye condition, and the need for hernia surgery. However, unique to Oisín was that he had jaundice for months, was a 'failure to thrive' baby, had blood-clotting issues, had suspected cystic fibrosis due to the lack of weight gain and constant chest and lung infections (thankfully it transpired it was an allergy to dairy) and is a terrible sleeper. Nevertheless, my claim to fame was that I did manage to breastfeed him at 14 weeks saving me months of breast pumping.

Having a premature baby can be life-changing. Five years down the road our lives still revolve around hospital appointments and clinics. Both boys are really prone to infections and are constantly sick, which can be very hard. I think I could have bought a little chateau in France with all the money we spend on drugs and GP visits. But for the love and joy they bring into our lives every day, it's priceless, and my husband and I absolutely treasure both our little prems.

Photographs of Cillian Fegan and Oisín Fegan.

Cillian, week 2 in the NICU   *Oisín, week 2 in the NICU*

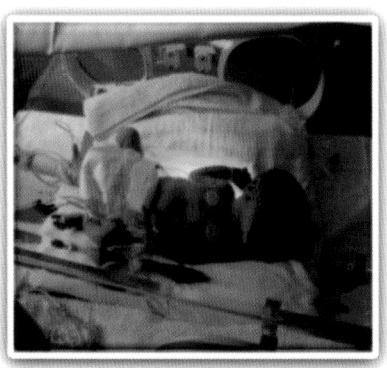
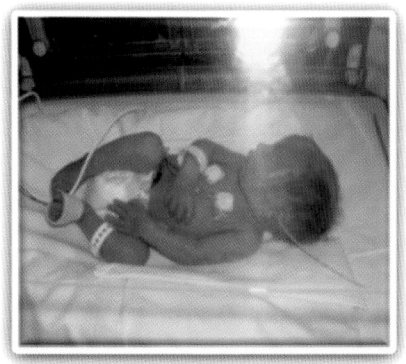

Cillian and Oisín sitting still for a   *The coolest four- and two-year-old*
second, age three and age one   *sitting on a Harley*

Conor Flynn (rest in peace) and Killian Flynn (27 weeks)

On 11 May our world was turned upside down when Killian and Conor were born 13 weeks premature, weighing 0.91 kg (2 lb) and 0.72 kg (1 lb 9 oz) respectively. The boys were born early due to TTTS. Our babies had a long road ahead, and we didn't know if they would make it. It was heartbreaking to look at them so small and surrounded by tubes. Both boys held their own for the first two days. Unfortunately, day 3 brought some devastating news. Conor's brain was badly damaged and irreparable. When he was one week old, Conor grew his angel wings and left us heartbroken.

During this time Killian was taken off his ventilator and had started feeding. We had to stay strong for him and also grieve for Conor. It was hard, but we managed it, and having a twin as an angel obviously was helping Killian as he was getting stronger every day.

Killian did have some setbacks. At two weeks he was put back on the ventilator due to an infection and a bleed on the lungs. Antibiotics and a blood transfusion put the fight back in him. When we got to hold him it was magical, and we cherished every second. At three weeks of age he was moved to ICU level 2 – a step closer to home. He was now only on oxygen and doing well. At one month, he took the big step and was transferred to Waterford from Dublin. He went on to need two more blood transfusions and treatment for fluid retention, and a heart murmur was detected, but he got through it all. At seven weeks he took his first bottle and was taken off oxygen and tube-feeding. At 11 weeks, Killian came home, and leaving the hospital he grinned so widely that we knew Conor was coming with us also.

Killian has just turned one and has already begun to walk. So far he shows no sign of any lasting problems. I believe Conor watches over him always, and that helps us with our grief. Killian has come a long way and is living proof that premature babies are stronger than we think. He needed laser eye surgery because of the length of time he was on oxygen but came through that. All the doctors are happy with him. He is our miracle baby, with his identical twin brother as his guardian angel.

Photographs of Conor Flynn and Killian Flynn.

Conor at 11.30 a.m. on the day he was born

Killian on the day he went home

Killian's first Christmas

Killian's first birthday

Conor Murtagh (30 weeks), Dylan Murtagh (33 weeks) and Ryan Murtagh (34 weeks)

When I found out I was pregnant on my first baby, we had just bought our first house. At our first scan we were given a due date of 22 January, which was great timing as our house was due to be completed three months before the due date. The week of the house move I began to feel light-headed and dizzy, which I put down to the move. However, when I went for my check-up, I was admitted as my blood pressure was elevated and I had protein in my urine. I was only 25 weeks pregnant and had never had a hospital stay before. I was administered steroids to develop the baby's lungs and was put on blood-pressure tablets. I ended up staying in hospital from October until December.

On 4 December, due to pre-eclampsia, I was scheduled to have a Caesarean section. My husband arrived, dressed in scrubs, and Dylan was born at 33 weeks, weighing 1.62 kg (3 lb 9 oz). He was so small and precious; I only caught a glimpse of him as he was rushed to the NICU to be ventilated. I was in shock and just wanted to hold my baby. Dylan was given a brain scan, and it showed a shadow on his brain. I didn't get to hold or see him until the next day. Dylan was moved onto assisted breathing with the help of CPAP. Slowly, day by day, he began to put on weight and get stronger. Dylan was finally allowed home in January, and luckily he has had no medical conditions since – except mild asthma. Dylan is now seven years old and is the tallest in his class.

After five years of trying to conceive again, we sought medical assistance as I have polycystic ovarian syndrome. We discovered in June that we were expecting a baby, and words cannot describe how delighted we were. My chances of developing pre-eclampsia were one in 1,000, so I didn't worry at all. I felt great until Christmas Eve when at a scheduled hospital check-up it was revealed that my blood pressure was sky-high. I was immediately sent to the Coombe in Dublin for admission, heartbroken to be leaving Dylan at home on Christmas Eve. I was again given steroids to develop the baby's lungs and monitored closely.

After another long stay in hospital, my blood pressure went out of control, and Ryan was delivered at 34 weeks, on 16 January, weighing 1.73 kg (3 lb 13 oz). Like his brother, he was rushed to NICU, where he was put on CPAP to help with his breathing. After 24 hours, he was transferred to the Rotunda Hospital in Dublin, due to lack of space in the Coombe. We spent the next few weeks in the Rotunda, where Ryan progressed rapidly. Ryan was discharged home three weeks later with no medical conditions and is now two years old. He is our little monkey.

Very soon after Ryan's birth I started to feel unwell and discovered I was pregnant again. Due to my history I was monitored very closely. When I was 25 weeks pregnant I began to experience dizzy spells and started seeing black spots. I was admitted to hospital for another long stay, but this time my condition deteriorated very fast, and I started to have fits. On 28 June, at 30 weeks, my miracle baby Conor was born, weighing 1.45 kg (3 lb 3 oz). Conor was very sick and was taken to the NICU and ventilated. He had four holes in his heart and had a heart murmur.

Four days later, on my birthday, we were told that Conor had caught an infection and that the next 24 hours were critical. We were also told that Conor's bowels might be reversed. He would have to have tests done as there was a black discharge coming from his stomach. I never prayed or cried so hard in all my life. We were called into a meeting and told that Conor was very weak and had stopped breathing during the night. We were terrified that we were going to lose him. After five long black days Conor started to improve.

He was finally allowed home, where he was housebound. Once a month a nurse would call to our home and would administer an injection to Conor to boost his immune system, and he had regular physiotherapy sessions, which he still attends. He still requires further hearing and heart exams, but luckily three of the holes in his heart have closed spontaneously. We are hopeful that the one remaining hole will close in time. Conor has just turned one and is a lovable bundle of joy. Words cannot describe the love we have for our three boys. They are our pride and joy, each born so early, yet so different in every way.

Photographs of Conor Murtagh, Dylan Murtagh and Ryan Murtagh.

Dylan at three weeks old

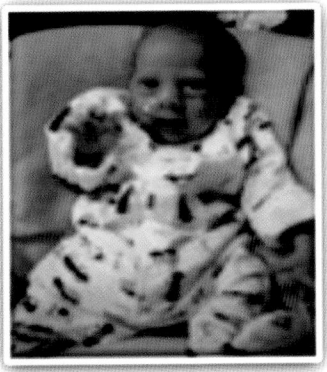

Ryan at two weeks old

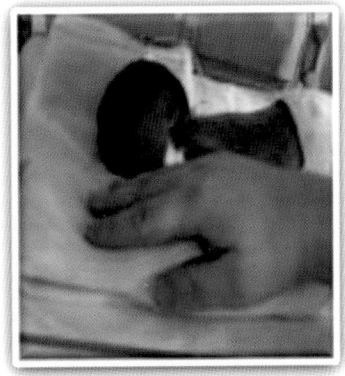

Conor at 19 days old

Dylan all grown up at seven years

∞

Craig Dowling (31 weeks)

Craig was born on St Stephen's Day at 31 weeks by emergency Caesarean section, weighing 1.64 kg (3 lb 10 oz). Born with RDS, resuscitation and ventilation were required at birth. Craig was brought to the NICU and seemed to be holding his own, but over the next few days things started to unravel for him. He began to have a lot of apnoeas and subsequently was diagnosed with NEC, a serious bowel condition. The following 48 hours were awful. It was such a major scare and shock to try and get our heads around.

After a few weeks, much earlier than we anticipated, Craig was moved out of NICU and into the SCBU. He was found to have a left-side-only congenital cataract and a micro-ophthalmic eye, for which surgery was the only option. In the meantime, his eye would have to be shielded, resulting in patching most of the time. There was also a query as to whether the other eye was healthy or if surgery could be performed successfully.

At long last we got a call one day to say that Craig was ready to go home. Our delight, however, was short-lived as Craig wasn't home two weeks when his apnoeas got much worse. This resulted in his admission to Our Lady's Children's Hospital, Crumlin. He went through a series of tests but no real reason could be found for his condition. A blood transfusion was also needed at this stage. Then a decision had to be made on whether Craig was fit enough for his eye surgery. It was decided that the surgery was an absolute necessity and should be completed as soon as possible, so Craig was scheduled as an in-patient for the operation to remove the cataract and to size a contact lens. Craig wore a contact lens for the first year of his life, which was a distressing time for all involved. Craig's health would improve for a few weeks and then suddenly deteriorate without any warning. We then had added problems with his contact lens and cornea abrasions. All measurements and assessments had to be done under anaesthetic which meant trying to fit Craig in between chest infections and courses of steroids, which proved to be very difficult. There were also queries over the hearing in Craig's left ear, which thankfully seems to be OK now. One of Craig's elective surgeries was the insertion of a lens into his eye, which was a success: no more contact lenses. Now we just have to try to get him to wear his patch and glasses every day.

Unfortunately, things didn't keep going well for Craig, and the apnoeas began to reoccur, resulting in numerous admissions to Crumlin and the National Children's Hospital in Tallaght for tests and re-tests. All the problems under the sun turned up at one stage or another, with oesophageal reflux, food intolerances, Rotavirus, pneumonia, unexplained blood in his urine, crystals in his urine, abnormal blood-clotting factors . . . the list is endless. Craig now looks for his aloe-vera juices every morning, which he takes no problem, one juice for his bowel and another to keep any asthma under control. He has come off most of his medication, and hopefully this will become a permanent thing in the future. Craig knows that thermometers are really phones and that stethoscopes are for tickling people, so maybe he will develop an interest in the medical profession. In meantime, however, when these things go missing on the wards they are normally found in Craig's room.

Craig is now three and a half years old and is doing well physically. We still have outpatient appointments and reviews which will be ongoing – some into his adult life. Physiotherapy is ongoing also due to premature spine resulting in bad muscle tone. He has gone from being a baby who was institutionalised, who didn't want cuddles and wouldn't take a bottle unless he was in the same spot with no one else in the room to a totally different child. He is now a little rascal and is the most affectionate little guy who gives brilliant hugs and kisses and knows how to work a room even at his age. He is totally besotted by Minnie Mouse since we went to Disneyland Paris last year and copies and idolises his big brother Oisin. Craig is a determined little man who can fight his corner – he has been a fighter since the minute he was born. The nurses who looked after him in the NICU often said that he made liars out of them by doing much better than they ever expected. Hopefully this will continue for the rest of Craig's life and he will always exceed expectations and keep fighting for whatever he wants.

Photographs of Craig Dowling.

Craig's very first picture

Craig in January 2010

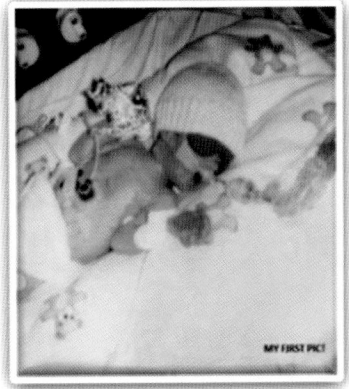

Craig with his big brother Oisin

Craig patrolling the streets

Daniel Burke (25 weeks)

Daniel was born at 25 weeks on 6 December, weighing 0.77 kg (1 lb 11 oz). He was ventilated for a few hours and then put onto CPAP for two months. I got to hold him for the first time when he was nine days old. I was so scared because he was so tiny. I was afraid I would break him, but after I held him the first time I did kangaroo care every chance I got. His daddy didn't get to experience a cuddle until he was six weeks old.

Day 17 was when Daniel's fight to be in this world started in earnest. He developed septicaemia and was ventilated for 10 days as he was very ill. We had one good week after the septicaemia and he became ill again. This time it was a lot more serious: he had NEC. The antibiotics he was given didn't work. He was given an hour to live, and we were heartbroken. He was rushed to another hospital for surgery to remove part of his bowel. By the time he got there he had deteriorated so much that he was operated on in the corner of ICU with just a curtain around him.

He had an ileostomy bag fitted, but we didn't mind. He was alive, and that was all that mattered. It was very scary for us learning to change the bag, but it was second nature to us by the time we brought him home. He was put on a special formula to help him gain weight. In total, Daniel spent 112 days in NICU. He came home weighing 1.96 kg (4 lb 5 oz). After three weeks at home he had not gained any weight, so he was readmitted. Our little boy was a mystery to the doctors. He had numerous tests done and nothing showed up, so he was taken off all feeds and put on a TPN drip.

Daniel got septicaemia again and kept catching different infections. He had blood and platelet transfusions on a weekly basis. After an MRI and sweat tests, he was eventually diagnosed with short bowel syndrome. He had IV lines fitted on both sides of his neck for antibiotics, but as he was so small his veins weren't strong enough and they collapsed. There were weights attached to them, but they made it so difficult to hold and cuddle him, so we had to be extra careful when picking him up. He had to go back into theatre to have a central line fitted into his chest, but his ileostomy bag was on the same side, which meant he would be open to infections.

It was decided then that a surgeon would remove the ileostomy bag because of the increased likelihood of infections. We weren't expecting this at all, and we were shocked really. The surgery took hours. It was the longest day of my life, sitting waiting on news. That evening I could hear a very familiar cry coming down the corridor. My poor little baby was in a terrible state. His morphine drip hadn't kicked in. It was heart-wrenching to hear him cry in pain. I cried with him. All I wanted to do was pick him up and give him a cuddle and take his pain away, but we couldn't even do that. It's very hard to sit helpless watching your child in pain. It's something no parent should ever have to experience.

That night Daniel was allowed 1 ml of formula after being starved for six weeks, and then every three hours it was increased until he was having 150 ml. This was a huge milestone for Daniel and for us. It was also a very emotional time because we knew we were finally going to get our baby home for good. After almost seven months in hospital, we finally brought our baby home, weighing 3.18 kg (7 lb). He has some long-term problems that he will always have. He has CLD, bronchiolitis and will always suffer problems with his bowel, but he's here and that's all that matters to us.

Daniel is adored by his older sister Nikki and brother Jamie and, of course, by us. He shows such determination in everything he does. Doctors told us he wouldn't walk until he was at least two years old, but on 13 May – seven months ahead of schedule – he stood up and off he went, and I don't think he's actually sat down since. He is an inspiration to us all, a true miracle baby.

Photographs of Daniel Burke.

The first time to see Daniel's beautiful face at 10 days

Ventilated at 17 days with septicaemia

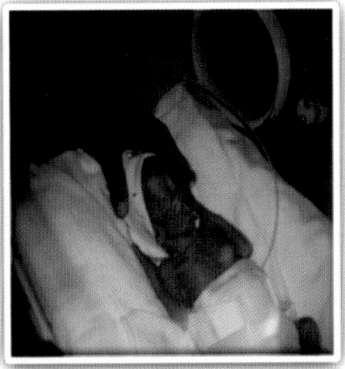
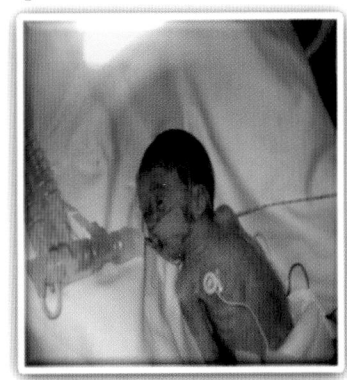

Cuddles with Daddy at six weeks

Daniel, a happy little boy

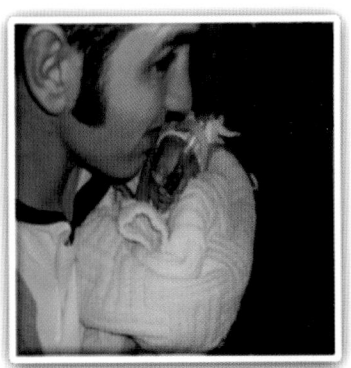

Daniel Campbell (29 weeks) and Samuel Campbell (25 weeks)

We are the very proud parents of two little boys born prematurely, eight years apart. The boys also have a big sister, Jenna, my first child, who was born right on time, so I had never even considered prematurity prior to having the boys. During my pregnancy with our older boy, Samuel, my only issue was morning sickness in the first trimester, and it was a huge shock to find myself in labour at just 25 weeks, with no apparent warning or reason. Thinking back now, I remember being so sure that I was actually in labour and luckily had no hesitation in heading straight to the hospital.

On arrival we were taken straight to the delivery suite. The neonatal staff were called and calmly told us what to expect after the baby was born. Samuel came into the world at 11.36 a.m. on 2 November, weighing in at 1.13 kg (2 lb 8 oz). He was immediately ventilated and taken to the NICU. I got to see him a little while later. I will never forget walking into the unit for the first time: the sounds, the smells and the sight of these tiny little people fighting so hard, it was like another world. All of the parents standing by their babies' incubators: some smiles, some very concerned faces. Our little man was in an incubator in the far corner of the room, so very tiny, yet so very strong.

Samuel bravely fought all the battles that he had to endure, of which there were many. He had numerous infections and needed blood transfusions and constant monitoring. I didn't get to hold him until he was three weeks old because he was so fragile. It was so difficult and frustrating only being able to touch his tiny hands. Every day I would hope that he was strong enough to come out for a cuddle, and eventually that day came. I will never forget holding him for the first time, I just didn't want to let him go.

We went through so many ups and downs during the 11 weeks that he spent in special care. Just before we were due to bring him home we were told that he had ROP and would require laser surgery. It was devastating, we were so close to home only to find out that he would have to move to another hospital for the procedure. Thankfully he came through the surgery very well, and we finally got to take him home to meet his big sister who had so patiently waited to meet him. It was one of the happiest days of my life.

Little did I know that eight years later I would be returning to the NICU once again with our second little man. Daniel was born on 2 December, weighing in at 1.45 kg (3 lb 4 oz) at 29 weeks' gestation. Amazingly, Daniel didn't need any ventilation but was on nasal-prongs oxygen for about three weeks. He was just as brave and strong as his big brother, and he fought hard every day to get home. All seemed to be going fine with Daniel. He had stayed free of infection and was feeding well and gaining weight at a steady level. It was wonderful to be able to take him out and cuddle him and to do kangaroo care with him.

However, after a week we got the news that Daniel had developed hydrocephalus as a result of a brain bleed and needed to be monitored closely for fluid. We hoped that, as it was a small bleed, it would clear in time and wouldn't require surgery. Daniel had to endure several spinal taps to clear the fluid building up on his brain, and, despite many attempts to relieve the pressure, the fluid continued to build and at six weeks of age he was taken to have a ventriculo-peritoneal shunt fitted.

In total, Daniel was in hospital for seven weeks. Thankfully he is doing very well and is now a strong, determined little two-year-old. He has had no problems with the shunt, and everything is working well.

Both of our boys have done so well. They both have had some minor issues to deal with, and it has and will continue to be a tough road ahead. Looking back on all that has happened and remembering all the things that they went through is incredibly emotional. For all those parents going through this journey now, we know exactly how they are feeling. When we look at how strong and brave our little boys are and what they have had to go through, it makes me feel incredibly proud. They are our little heroes.

Photographs of Daniel Campbell and Samuel Campbell.

Samuel at six weeks   *Daniel at three weeks*

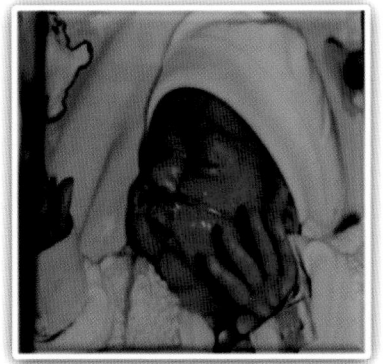
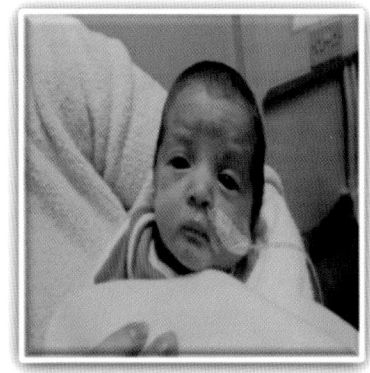

Samuel, all grown up at 10   *Daniel at two years*

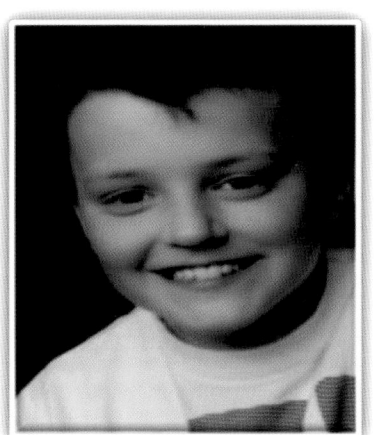

Daniel O'Brien (27 weeks)
and Tara O'Brien (36 weeks)

Seven weeks before my daughter was due, my wife Arlene developed a pregnancy-related complication and was admitted to University Hospital Galway. Three weeks later, our daughter Tara was born. The initial jubilation of her birth was overshadowed by the heartbreak of going home without her. The 11 days that she spent in the SCBU felt like an eternity. Machines were beeping, nurses were running, and babies were crying. The SCBU has a reassuring ambiance but is overwhelming nonetheless. Tara's stay was just another task for the medical staff, but it was quite traumatic for us as parents.

When we got the wonderful news that we were expecting a baby boy two years later, we were cautiously excited. What we didn't know was that Tara's little brother was going to be tiny. Nothing prepared us for what was around the corner. Almost six months into the pregnancy we attended a function. Arlene felt unwell during the meal. Within hours she was hospitalised. Suddenly it had become a matter of 'when' he would be delivered rather than 'if'. Eight days later, she had an emergency delivery, and Daniel O'Brien entered the world abruptly, 13 weeks before he was due.

He was wrapped in plastic and looked so delicate. He was sent immediately to intensive care. I was given a very brief opportunity to take a photograph of him as there was a very real chance that we would never see him alive again. Hours later, one of Daniel's lungs collapsed, and we were informed that our precious son might not survive. Daniel was fighting to breathe. Arlene's condition had worsened so she was transferred to the HDU at the other end of the hospital. She physically couldn't be with her newborn baby at a time when he really needed his mother. He fought hard and defied the odds even though he remained critical. I gained a whole new understanding of the word 'critical'. The hospital chaplin administered what can only be described as an 'emergency baptism', whereby he used a syringe and tap water to christen him. There were no godparents present, just a team of nurses who had seen it all before and will see it all again. Yet still there wasn't a dry eye in the room. Daniel needed constant monitoring and intervention. He was wired, plumbed and tubed. His tiny nappy was far too big for him. His first babysitter was a computer and an army of nurses.

Despite the trauma of his introduction to the world, it wasn't hard to see that Daniel was a handsome little man with determination in his eyes. One nurse quipped how tall he was even though my wedding ring could fit all the way up his arm. Some days he would show signs of improvement but then an alarm would trigger a stampede of medics to resuscitate him. One step forward, two steps back. Sometimes 20 steps back and one step forward. I gained a whole new perspective on life. What used to be important had become insignificant. We prayed that time would speed up rather than pass by at a snail's pace. I would jump frantically if the phone rang, and I was forever checking the battery levels and strength of the signal. A month after he was born, Arlene held Daniel for the first time. He was still attached to all sorts of machines, but we treasured the moment.

Whenever Daniel got blood transfusions I would watch in awe as he changed colour from grey to blue to rosy pink. Weeks passed, and he graduated from the incubator to a little plastic cot that resembled a basin. He still couldn't breathe on his own, but he was making great progress on the CPAP machine. Other babies came and went, but our little man had settled in. Daniel's status was downgraded from 'critical' to 'stable' to 'go home'. Before we knew it, Daniel was a whopping 100 days old. That was the day when they told us to get ready to bring him home to meet his sister Tara. After 105 days, we brought our boy home.

For Daniel's first birthday, he had a big party even though, as host, he was totally oblivious. Deep down, Daniel must know that he is special. He has a permanent smile and a wicked sense of humour. He is mischievous and robust yet loving and affectionate. He has enriched our lives beyond words. There is an ongoing array of appointments from physiotherapists to nutritionists to speech therapists to name just three, but Daniel has punched above his weight since the day he was born and will undoubtedly do so for the rest of his life. He is quite simply a little dude.

Photographs of Daniel O'Brien and Tara O'Brien.

Little Daniel greets the world   *A special kiss from Mammy*

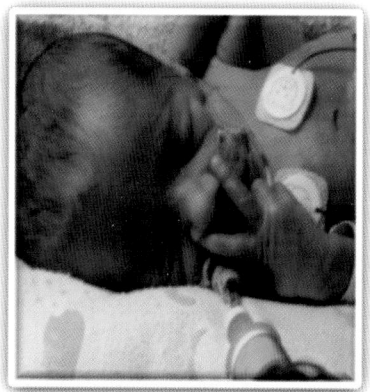   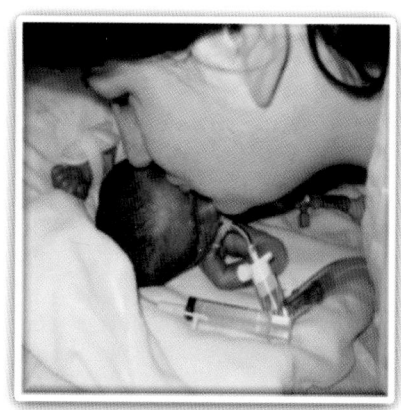

Daniel with a collapsed lung   *Best friends, big sister Tara*

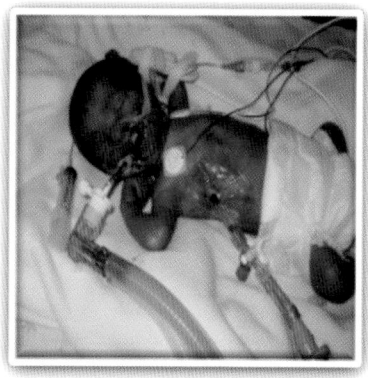   

Dean O'Sullivan (32 weeks)

Our son Dean was born at 32 weeks weighing 0.96 kg (2 lb 2 oz). He was growth restricted in the womb, which led to tests being carried out when I was 27 weeks pregnant. One of the tests performed was an amniocentesis test, which was to see if there were any chromosome defects. Five days later the results came back which told us our baby had Down Syndrome. It was a major shock as this was our first baby, but we got over it pretty quickly as all we wanted was our baby to come home with us no matter what. It was then we were told that Dean would be born premature as he wasn't growing correctly due to reverse blood flow. They told us that he would only weigh 0.6 kg (1 lb 5 oz). We had already found out previously that we were having a girl, so to add more drama it was an even greater shock when we were told the baby was in fact a boy.

I was admitted into hospital to have fetal heart monitoring for a week. On 26 March I felt something was wrong. I called the nurse and asked her to do another heart check, and there was no heartbeat. The doctor soon arrived and rushed me down to theatre. Dean was born at 4.54 p.m. They told us not to expect to hear him cry as he was so small, but he yelped. I didn't get to see him again until 6.00 a.m. the next morning. I got a shock: he was so tiny, smaller than I ever imagined. We called him 'Tom Thumb'.

Medical staff advised that he would require 100 per cent oxygen for a long time because his lungs were not developed. However, he only required 21 per cent oxygen for six hours and breathed unaided thereafter. He surprised them all. The nurses were fantastic and don't get enough recognition. They were not only taking care of the baby but were taking care of us as well. To have a premature baby is a scary thing. After spending all that time in the NICU and seeing those babies all fight for life, they really are angels.

After six weeks we got to take Dean home. He weighed 1.81 kg (4 lb). We waited so long for that day but when it arrived we were petrified in case we did something wrong. Luckily, we have all managed to settle down into our routine at home, and Dean is doing so well. He is a very happy little boy and we feel so lucky to have him. I wish that every person got a smile like I do from Dean every morning.

Photographs of Dean O'Sullivan.

Dean, two hours old

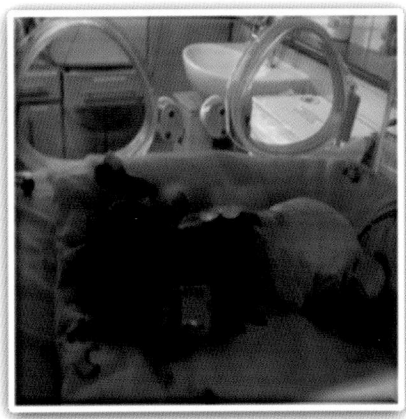

Dean, one day old

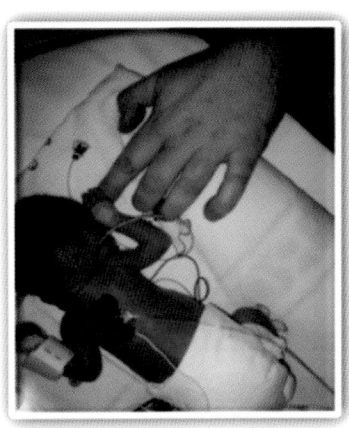

The day Dean went home

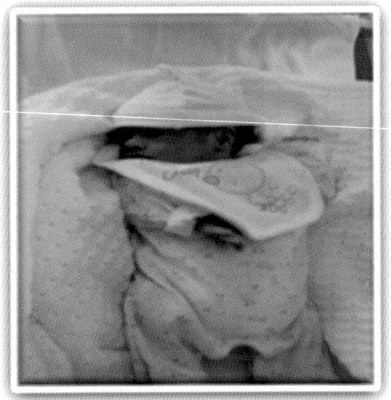

Dean at 13 months

Tiny Footprints

Declan Nolan (31 weeks), Dylan Nolan (32 weeks) and Laoise Nolan (34 weeks)

Throughout my first pregnancy with our daughter Laoise I suffered from hyperemesis. On most occasions this would stop between 13 and 19 weeks. However, mine was more persistent. I rarely left the hospital. Our daughter Laoise was delivered early by emergency Caesarean section at 34 weeks and 6 days on 20 May. She weighed in at 2.89 kg (6 lb 6 oz). Luckily she had no complications and only spent five days in the Coombe before she was discharged.

I suffered three miscarriages, then Dylan Thomas was born, nearly four years later, on 7 February. Dylan was born prematurely, at 32 weeks, as I had suffered from placenta previa. He weighed 2.13 kg (4 lb 11 oz). It was a traumatic birth. Even though I had gone into premature labour before, I had a feeling this was different as the pains weren't subsiding. I was having pains for most of the day and was being monitored. I had just arrived in the delivery suite when the placenta broke away. Panic arose around me and I knew it was bad. The only words I said until he was born were 'Please make my baby live' and 'Please don't let my baby die.' I repeated those words until Dylan was born. He was not breathing and had to be resuscitated at birth. I never heard him cry.

The first two days after his birth were extremely hard. Dylan had to be ventilated. In both the NICU and the SCBU, he had bi-lateral ventricle bleeds on his brain. He was on CPAP. He suffered from apnoea and bradycardias. When he was eventually discharged from hospital he came home on an MR10 respiratory monitor for his apnoeas. He spent five weeks in the Coombe Women and Infants University Hospital in Dublin, and for the first year of his life was in and out of the National Children's Hospital in Tallaght and Our Lady's Children's Hospital in Crumlin.

At first he was classed as being developmentally delayed. Since he was one, he was diagnosed with periventricular leukomalacia and cerebral palsy. He has low muscle tone and problems with his left leg. He has to wear specially adapted shoes to help counteract his low muscle tone. He still has night spasms and has problems with climbing small heights. Dylan is now two and a half and is doing well. He attends Enable Ireland and gets a lot of support there. He is a happy little man who is crazy about miniature cars and music.

Two years later, on 1 February, my third child Declan arrived. He was also born prematurely at 31 weeks. He weighed 1.67 kg (3 lb 11 oz). Declan was born with RDS. After the stress of Dylan's birth, I was put asleep for Declan's birth. He spent four weeks in the Coombe. After discharge he suffered from reflux and seizures. His care was transferred to Our Lady's in Crumlin. While he was there he had to be fed via a nasogastric tube. Declan is still fed nasogastrically and is waiting for a PEG. He has been diagnosed with evolving cerebral palsy – 'evolving' refers to the fact that over time the physical manifestations of the cerebral palsy are becoming more obvious – and he has high muscle tone quadriplegic cerebral palsy. He also has delayed myelination and has splints on both hands.

Like his brother, Declan attends Enable Ireland. Since he was born my life has changed dramatically. I had to learn how to look after Declan's nasogastric tube and how to do physiotherapy with him. Having two children with disabilities due to prematurity isn't easy. But I always believe where there is great love in a home there is everything. All three of them are treasures: the smiles, the giggles and the miracles that they are, I couldn't put into words how much they all mean to me.

Photographs of Declan Nolan, Dylan Nolan and Laoise Nolan.

Declan in the NICU

Dylan in the NICU

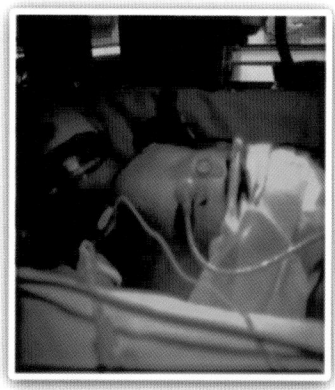

Laoise's first day at school

The three siblings together

Diarmaid Keane (26 weeks)

Our little miracle son, Diarmaid, was born on Friday, 23 October, at 9.45 p.m. by emergency Caesarean section in Mayo General Hospital in Castlebar. He weighed 0.97 kg (just over 2 lb) at 26 weeks and 6 days' gestation; he was 14 weeks early. One of the very surprising aspects of Diarmaid's birth was that I had only found out that I was pregnant three weeks prior to his delivery.

Diarmaid was transferred to the NMH in Dublin the following day for specialised care. Before he left, the hospital arranged for him to be baptised. It was the first time I really saw my little man, apart from the brief seconds in theatre before he was rushed off to SCBU. I was given a little Polaroid picture the nurses had taken for me, but it's not the same as seeing your baby in the flesh. The staff had arranged for Diarmaid to be wheeled out past my room on his way to the ambulance so I could say my goodbyes. It was the hardest thing I have ever had to do in my entire life, saying goodbye to my tiny little baby who should have been still snuggled up warm and safe inside of me.

It was awful to be in the maternity ward with all the other new mums and their babies while my little man was on the other side of the country. I was eventually discharged from Mayo General Hospital and headed straight up to Dublin to be at my son's side. Diarmaid spent just over four weeks in the care of the wonderful staff in the NICU in Holles Street. I spent as much time as I possibly could at his side. Sometimes I just looked at him, sometimes I talked to him, and whenever possible I looked after him, like changing a nappy. The highlight of my day would be when I was allowed to hold him. To be able to hold my baby, doing skin-to-skin contact or kangaroo care, felt wonderful. Diarmaid seemed to enjoy those moments too and still loves his cuddles with Mummy.

We were one of the lucky families: Diarmaid progressed day by day. He spent just less than a week on a breathing ventilator, then he was moved onto assisted breathing with CPAP. He battled and fought everything that was thrown at him from blood transfusions to an endless battle with MRSA. We were eventually given the go-ahead for him to be transferred back to Mayo General Hospital. This was the first milestone we wanted to achieve.

Leaving Holles Street, we had a mixture of emotions. We were happy to be moving closer to home, and we imagined how life would be much easier once we were there. But I was fearful of leaving the NICU I knew so well and the staff who knew Diarmaid so well at this stage also. Strangely enough, I had almost started to feel comfortable in my surroundings while in the unit. There was a long journey in an ambulance to cope with but I knew Diarmaid would not have been transferred if he wasn't able for the journey. As it transpired, the staff in the SCBU in Castlebar were just as wonderful as the Dublin NICU. They soon got to know Diarmaid so well, and I could see as he was getting older that his personality was developing.

Diarmaid spent the next six weeks in the SCBU getting stronger. He put on weight, learnt to breathe without the help of oxygen and learnt to bottle-feed. Eventually we got the news we had been waiting for, and after 10 weeks Diarmaid was discharged home. Our little fighter came home with his mother and father on 30 December. It was an amazing start to the New Year. He weighed 2.55 kg (5 lb 10 oz) at 36 weeks and 4 days' gestation.

Diarmaid is now smiling and laughing, chatting away in his own baby way. He is walking, climbing, playing with his toys and sometimes even throwing and breaking things. He is your typical toddler who loves his cartoons. He is a very strong-willed, determined little man, but I guess he had to be, he had such a big fight on his tiny hands. Diarmaid brings such wonder and pleasure to our lives every single day. He makes me laugh and smile at least once a day, and sometimes he makes me want to pull my hair out, but that's all part of being a parent. There are days that I almost forget everything we have been through and what was all so familiar in those days is becoming a distant memory.

Photographs of Diarmaid Keane.

Diarmaid, two days old

Diarmaid's very first Christmas in the SCBU

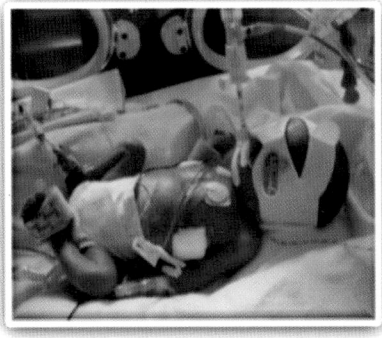

Diarmaid on Mammy and Daddy's wedding day

Diarmaid playing at 20 months

Dion O'Callaghan (30 weeks)

My waters broke at 24 weeks, and I was kept in hospital. Dion was born in June 2008 by emergency Caesarean at 30 weeks. During Dion's birth his right lung collapsed, and when I came round I was handed a photo of my baby and told that he was in theatre. He required an operation to inflate his lung as two previous attempts had not worked. I was told that if I got a call from theatre that Dion would have about 10 minutes to live. I received the call, and the priest gave the last rites to Dion and baptised him. Amazingly, during this baptism Dion's condition stabilised and remained that way.

Dion spent 10 weeks in SCBU. When he was born he could not breathe properly, nor could he swallow or cry. I was allowed my first cuddle three weeks after he was born. Dion was beautiful, with a mop of dark hair, although he had no fingernails or eyelashes.

During Dion's stay in SCBU he contracted meningitis and had four blood transfusions and antibiotics. He was allowed home after his due date, 13 August, when he passed the 'car seat test'. He was placed in a car seat, and if his heart rate was stable for a specific period of time he could go home. It took three attempts before we realised the car seat doubled up as a rocker and was not steady on the floor. Dion was allowed home the next day.

The first year of Dion's life was difficult, and he was admitted to hospital two weeks before Christmas with bronchitis and was given two days to live. Dion is three now, and I would not swap him for the world. I love him very much, but it is frightening when you have a premature baby. Being separated from your baby for 10 weeks was the worst experience.

Photographs of Dion O'Callaghan.

Just after Dion's lung collapsed

First precious cuddle with Mammy

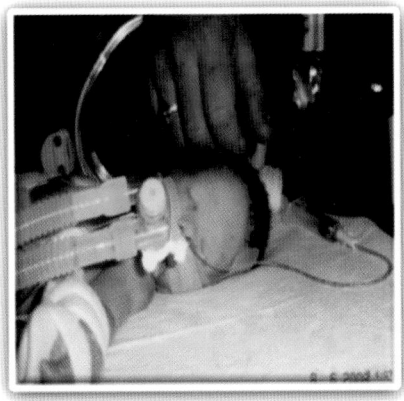

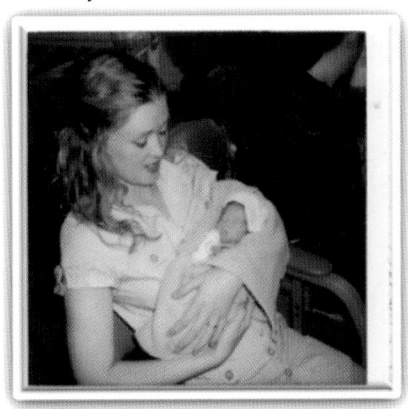

Dion's first Christmas

Dion with his big brother Morgan

ɔß

Éadaoin Ellen O'Sullivan (29 weeks)

The first six months of pregnancy were uneventful, without even morning sickness, but when I was admitted to hospital with pre-eclampsia at 26 weeks and 4 days, that all changed. The consultant advised me that I might have to deliver any day. During three weeks in hospital, seven trips to the HDU meeting the neonatologist and visiting the NICU, we began to come to terms with the fact that our baby would be born very early and ill.

At 29 weeks and 6 days, Éadaoin Ellen O'Sullivan was born by emergency Caesarean section at 1.36 a.m. on 26 October, weighing 1.08 kg (2 lb 6 oz). She was so tiny, about the length of a ruler, and my husband's wedding ring easily fitted on her arm. Although my husband visited her many times, it was at least 24 hours before I saw her and another eight days before I held her. It was surreal to think that this tiny baby, locked in an incubator and fighting for her life, was our little girl.

We quickly adapted to the new world of the NICU. We were washing our hands so often they were raw, no longer wearing our wedding rings in case they would carry infection. My husband and I visited every day, often more than once, spending up to 12 hours at a time at Éadaoin's incubator. At first we were not allowed to hold her, so we just watched her breathing in and out, something of a miracle in our eyes. I expressed my breastmilk for her so I became a regular visitor to the expressing room, or 'milking parlour' as it was affectionately known by the fellow mothers who used it every three or four hours. Quickly getting over our shyness, it became a great place to meet mothers and discuss our babies' progress and diagnoses. I made friends for life there in

Catherine and Katherine, as we got to know each other and our babies.

Éadaoin was strong and brave from the outset, and relatively well; however, she still had challenges. She needed CPAP to help her breathe and developed potentially fatal NEC. Éadaoin also had a heart murmur, a PDA and two IV antibiotics in her first two weeks. She had many blood draws from her tiny, bruised hands and feet and was fed via tube, initially through her navel, then graduating to nasogastric tubes in her nose and mouth.

Some good times stand out too. Cuddle times were so special, made more so because of their rarity. Premature babies benefit from a special type of cuddle known as 'kangaroo care', where your naked or partially clothed baby is placed inside your clothing to have skin-to-skin contact with their parent. I spent hours doing kangaroo care during the day, and my husband loved to have his turn for cuddles when he came from work – it is definitely as therapeutic for the parents as for the baby. The NICU had these lovely big brown chairs which seemed so relaxing. We would sit with Éadaoin cuddled into us on these chairs and we could no longer even hear the alarms which were the constant background noise. Doctors' rounds in the morning were also a good time, even if there were difficult messages to hear. We craved information on our daughter's progress. When the Professor was doing rounds, he wrote down his observations for us, always starting with 'Éadaoin's a beautiful girl.' I loved that medical diagnosis! Under the guidance of the fantastic nurses we learnt to change our little baby's nappy via the two circular doorways of the incubator and then dress her in the tiniest vests and hats. It was great to finally feel there was something we could do for her.

Éadaoin spent six weeks in the NICU while she learnt how to digest EBM, starting on 0.45 ml per hour, and how to keep warm without the help of the incubator. She graduated to the

SCBU, and, two weeks later, weighing 2.35 kg (5 lb 3 oz), we got the perfect Christmas present when Éadaoin came home on 20 December. We couldn't drive to our house due to snow so we quickly walked her home on the coldest day on record. Now nine months old (six months corrected), Éadaoin is a beautiful, funny, happy baby. She drinks big bottles, eats so much, sleeps all night, rolls around and is trying to sit on her own. We feel very proud and blessed to have such a wonderful daughter by any standards, but especially with Éadaoin's difficult start. We also know how lucky we are with the fabulous care she received, and continues to receive, at CUMH.

Photographs of Éadaoin Ellen O'Sullivan.

Éadaoin at eight days old

Éadoin at nine days old

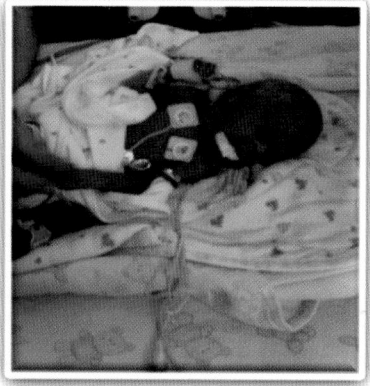

Éadaoin at six months

Éadaoin at seven months

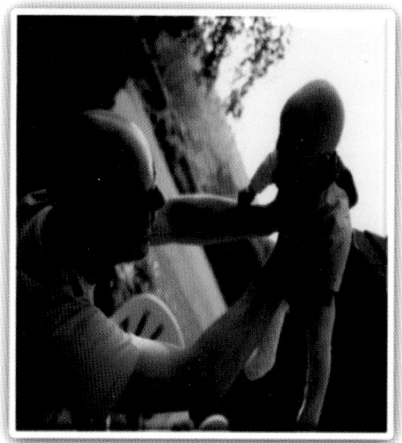

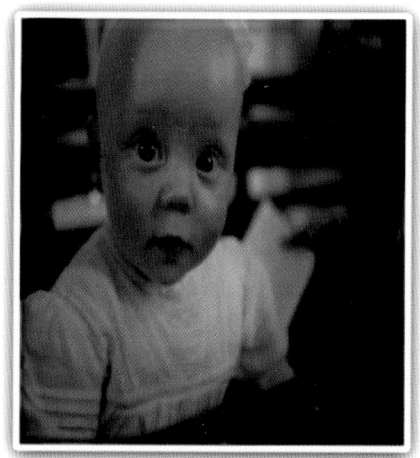

Eli Arthur Furlong (30 weeks)

At week seven, I was diagnosed with a suspected miscarriage after being rushed to A&E with pain. Just before I had the D&C, I asked for a repeat scan, which, much to our amazement, revealed our little man waving back at a room of shocked people. From then on he was monitored closely.

My anomaly scan at 21 weeks showed that he was three weeks behind in some places and more in others. I was classed as a high-risk pregnancy, and every week we got further was a bonus. They diagnosed me with IUGR, and from then on I had regular growth scans to monitor baby's progress. The outlook was never good, and I was told at some appointments that the baby wouldn't survive for long as medical staff were unsure why he stopped growing. All the chromosomal problems were discussed, and the medical team suggested an amniocentesis at 23 weeks. This carried a risk of starting labour, and I didn't want to put my baby at any more unnecessary risk, so I declined. It was decided at 28 weeks that I should be admitted to the NMH in Dublin for more specialised care, and after a chat with my paediatrician I tried to aim for the magic 31 weeks. They say after 31 weeks babies have a better chance, and it was through researching this fact that I discovered Irish Premature Babies. Being very naive on how or what a premature baby was, I emailed them and got a buddy who had previously gone through a similar experience. It was more the unknown that was frightening, and to talk to someone who went through it too, without all the medical jargon, was something I was very grateful for.

At 30 weeks, D-Day arrived, and the baby was better out than in. I spent the last night in hospital crying my eyes out, because I knew once baby was born I could no longer look after him and would have to hand his care over to someone else. All the prodding and medical intervention I was receiving was just going to be transferred from me to him, like the twice-daily scans where they couldn't catch his tiny heart and I would spend hours hooked up waiting to get a clear trace. I got about 30 scans (and I was afraid I would only get the one scan!) where I watched him grow from a fetus to a tiny baby and felt I knew him before he even arrived. From here on in I was putting my baby's life in someone else's hands and the harsh reality hadn't even hit me yet.

Eli Arthur was born on 23 September by Caesarean section at 1.02 p.m., weighing 0.88 kg (1 lb 15 oz). I saw a photo my husband took of him two hours later. 'He's perfect,' he smiled, 'tiny but perfect,' showing me a photo of a red wrinkly baby covered in tubes and wires, and my heart was lost from that moment on. The doctors were amazed at the fight Eli had in him. He didn't need any ventilation from birth and was only on CPAP for one day. On day 3 we got to hold him and do skin-to-skin contact. These kangaroo sessions couldn't last long as Eli couldn't regulate his own body temperature and also needed to be under the lights for his jaundice. But those few minutes every day made sitting by an incubator for hours on end bearable.

They say babies don't smile for the first few weeks of their lives, but I have photos of Eli smiling on my chest, and we knew he needed those cuddles as much as I did. No family could visit him so I used to describe to them how big he was: put your hand out, add a tennis-ball head, sausage arms and legs the size of a small water bottle. Even looking back on photos now I find it hard to believe.

During those weeks we watched Eli's ears move up from his neck, watched as he grew nipples overnight and watched him lose the downy hair that covered his body. We knew we were nothing but privileged to have him in our lives, a little miracle who had survived. For every step forward you take two back in intensive care, and it was not until after 10 long weeks, with two blood transfusions, four doses of antibiotics, catheters in the head, leg and arm and his little body covered in pinholes, that Eli finally made it home, just before Christmas and five days after his actual due date – on his daddy's birthday – weighing 2.35 kg (5 lb 3 oz). Ten months on and he is still in 0–3-month clothes, a tiny little man with a big personality, and I wouldn't change a thing.

Photographs of Eli Arthur Furlong.

Eli was two weeks old and the same size as his tatty bear

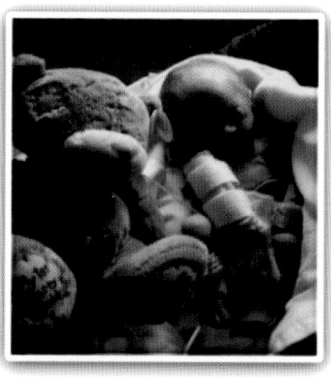

Eli at home two days after been released from hospital

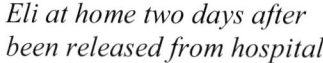

Eli on his zero birthday, weighing 5 lb

Eli at 10 months, just learnt to sit up

Emily Cleere (34 weeks)

Emily was born by emergency Caesarean section in October at 34 weeks. She weighed 3.49 kg (7 lb 11 oz), which made her one of the biggest in special care. My husband went with her to the SCBU while I remained in recovery. It was such a different experience from when I had my first daughter as she never left my sight the whole time I was in hospital.

When I got out of recovery I found out that Emily was doing well but needed oxygen. Later in the day the paediatrician told me they might have to transfer Emily to another hospital as she was very tired and her colour was not great. I had not seen her for more than a few seconds. The doctor decided to intubate Emily to try and rest her. This worked well, and she came back to tell me later that night that Emily was much improved. The next morning I got to see her properly for the first time.

She was in an incubator and had a lot of tubes and machines. She was really beautiful, and even though she was a good weight she was so small. Every time I went to see her I held my breath, half afraid I would see the doctors crowded round her incubator after something untoward happening to her. After a few days I was allowed home. It was the most unnatural feeling to leave her there. We phoned first thing every morning to enquire about her condition, and although she was always pretty stable we were nervous making the phone call.

We visited Emily a few times every day and got the chance to feed and change her as she got stronger. After nine days she was moved to a cot and she got to wear a babygro for the first time. It was a big day for her. She was getting closer to coming home, but she was slow to feed and tired very easily.

Tiny Footprints

She would go great some days, taking three or four feeds in a row from a bottle only to tire herself out so much that she needed the next few feeds from the tube again.

After 26 days Emily was allowed home. She was up to over 3.6 kg (7 lb 15 oz). We woke her every three to four hours to feed and she never looked back. She is now nine months old and is absolutely gorgeous. Her big sister Gracie is mad about her and is looking forward to the day when Emily can run around with her.

Photographs of Emily Cleere.

Emily, one day old

Emily, one week old

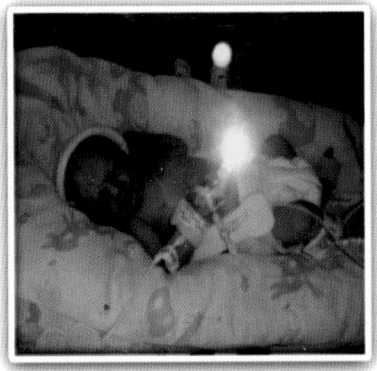

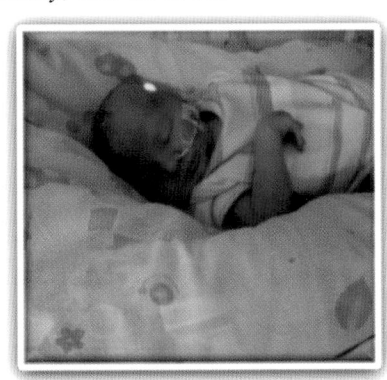

Emily, six weeks old

Emily, nine months old

Tiny Footprints

∝

Emily Kavanagh (rest in peace)
and Heidi Kavanagh (29 weeks)

Twins, Seriously? You've got to be kidding me. We've an 18-month-old at home, how are we going to cope? The tears started to fall, I couldn't believe it. We could never manage, let alone afford, two more children at this time. Little did we know, our lives were certainly going to change, but for very different reasons. Over time, it was discovered our identical twin girls were monoamniotic, a rare occurrence – in fact one in a million. Twin pregnancies. They were both in the same amniotic sac, therefore a danger to each other from the outset. The mortality rate is 50 per cent, so I was closely monitored and constantly reminded by the hospital that they could die at any moment. The main reason for death would be cord entanglement, as without this special protective sac the babies are a danger to themselves and each other. The longer the pregnancy continued, the higher the risk.

My initial reaction of how would we cope had now changed to how would we cope without our beautiful girls? They were soldiers in our eyes, little fighters already. Such a hard start to life, and they were still in the womb, they hadn't even ventured into the world. Twice a week I was scanned, and twice a week I'd see two precious heartbeats, 20 fingers and 20 toes, growing and developing. They were defying the odds.

That was until 8 June, the day our lives were turned upside down. A routine scan, at almost 30 weeks, showed only one of my precious heartbeats. One of my soldiers had been taken from us. I was in a daze. I had known it could happen at any stage, but I chose not to believe it. The girls appeared to be doing so well. The race was on to save our other little girl as she was making herself anaemic trying to save her sister. After numerous meetings with specialists, the decision was made to have an emergency section to save her. She would be 10 weeks premature, but we all felt the risks in the womb greatly outweighed the challenges in the outside world.

My girls were born at 4.30 p.m. that afternoon. Emily was born sleeping, weighing 1.13 kg (2 lb 8 oz), perfect in every way. She just looked so peaceful. Heidi was born screaming, weighing 1.42 kg (3 lb 1 oz), ready to face the next big battle of her life on the outside. They were just beautiful. We cuddled Emily for hours, days in fact, trying to keep her warm and willing her to just open her eyes. She was so perfect. It just didn't seem real. We had one girl fighting for her life in the NICU while the other was in our arms but lifeless. We took lots of pictures, received prints of her hands and feet and a lock of her hair and had a lovely burial ceremony for her on 14 June.

Heidi was made stable and fed vitamins through her belly button for the first couple of days. I didn't get to meet her until the morning after her birth, and it was so surreal. We knew they were tiny as we had held Emily, but Heidi just seemed so helpless, lost, in this big incubator. The days turned into weeks, and she had good days and bad days. She survived so many medical interventions and complications: intubation, CPAP, two blood transfusions, MRSA and a blood infection. Heidi was such a determined little girl, she was fighting it all – and winning. I spent every possible minute with her, watching her every move, watching her grow and thrive before me. I became obsessed with expressing my breastmilk, as I could see the benefits right before my eyes.

My life revolved around the NICU and getting Heidi home to meet her family and friends. It was such an emotional roller-coaster, trying to grieve, to be strong for Heidi and to not let our other little girl at home suffer from our current predicament. I kept a journal, a day-to-day account of

Tiny Footprints

everything Heidi went through in the hospital, all the treatments she received, little comments on how we were feeling, how great the staff were and how big she was getting. I found this very therapeutic; it was like my own little counselling session every day.

Eight weeks later, the big day finally arrived. I could have screamed from the rooftops when they gave us the news we'd so eagerly waited to hear. Yes, we were worried. Could we manage with such a small, delicate baby? Would she survive without her machines? Of course we would, she was our daughter, and we were the best people to take care of her. On 29 July, our fighter was discharged, a whole 2.27 kg (5 lb) of gorgeousness. She is a true miracle, loved by all, especially by her big sister Zoe and guarded by her twin Emily, from her playground in the sky.

Photographs of Heidi Kavanagh.

Heidi, two days old

Heidi, one week old

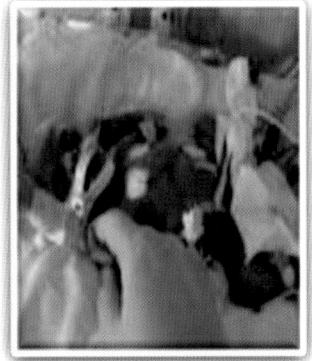

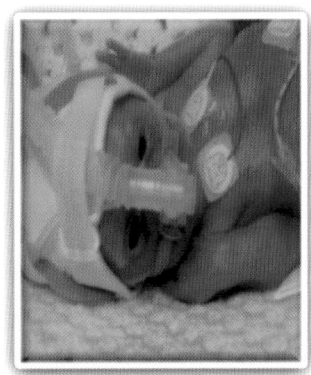

Heidi at nine months

Heidi with big sister Zoe

Emily Molloy (30 weeks),
Kevin Molloy (34 weeks) and
Ryan Molloy and Adam Molloy (35 weeks)

When we decided to try for a baby, it happened fairly quickly, and our first child was due in March. It was a normal pregnancy initially, with just the usual symptoms of tiredness and a little nausea, but overall I progressed as normal. At 30 weeks I noticed my feet were quite swollen but just put this down to the pregnancy. It was only when I went to my doctor for a routine check-up and she checked my blood pressure and urine that we found out there was a problem. My blood pressure was sky-high, and there was protein in my urine. I was told to go directly to the hospital and was admitted straight away. I had no idea how serious things were at that stage but soon realised as things began to happen very fast.

The medical team were all around me, scanning my baby, hooking me up to a drip and connecting me to various monitors. They asked if I knew what pre-eclampsia was, and at this point my husband fainted and had to be carried over to the bed opposite to be woken up. I was given steroids to strengthen the baby's lungs and monitored closely over the next two days. Then, on a Sunday evening at 7 o'clock, I was told I was going to have my baby. It was 9 January. I was whisked down to surgery, given a general anaesthetic, and at 9.17 p.m., at just 30 weeks' gestation, Emily was born by emergency Caesarean section weighing 1.45 kg (3 lb 3 oz). My husband was told to follow our daughter's incubator down to the SCBU as I was brought round and told that I had given birth to a little girl. I was sent to intensive care as a precaution, and a short while later my husband came in with a photo of our tiny girl, attached to lots of wires and tubes. It was a big shock to us both. The paediatrician explained that Emily was doing well but had been ventilated to help her breathing. I was so scared for her and felt so upset that I couldn't even get to see her at that point.

On Tuesday morning, two days after the birth, I was stable enough to be wheeled down to see my little baby for the first time. I was told what to expect, but nothing really prepared me. I can't describe the instant love I felt for this little tiny baby who was nothing more than a little bag of bones. I was so upset to see her like this, but she had already been taken off the ventilator, and although we didn't realise it at the time she was already proving to be quite a little fighter. They asked us if we would like to baptise her, and we did. A nurse was our witness, and I held her little hand as she was baptised. I was put into a ward that day full of new mums and their babies, and, although I had lots of family around me, I felt very alone without Emily.

I expressed my breastmilk for her to be tube-fed as she was still too small to suck, and we had our first cuddle when she was about three days old. I remember being so nervous at the time, holding this tiny little thing, but it was so lovely to be able to finally have her in my arms. The day I had to go home and leave Emily behind inevitably arrived, and I cried as I left the hospital with my husband. The next few weeks were a blur, but around three weeks later I finally realised that we would actually be bringing our little girl home. She went from strength to strength, and after six long weeks we were finally told we could bring her home. She came home weighing 2.27 kg (5 lb), and although we thought she was huge, other people couldn't believe how tiny she was. We were told Emily might not reach all of her developmental milestones on time but she proved everyone wrong.

Five years later I went on to have a little boy, Kevin, who was born six weeks early. Kevin was born at 34 weeks, weighing 2.78 kg (6 lb 2 oz), spent two weeks in hospital and did not need ventilation. Five years after Kevin, I had twin boys, Ryan and Adam, who were five weeks premature. Ryan weighed 2.38 kg (5 lb 4 oz) and Adam 2.64 kg (5 lb 13.5 oz). They were born at 35 weeks, but there was no hospital stay or visit to SCBU. Our experience with Emily prepared us so well for having three other premature babies.

I have shed lots of tears while reliving these memories in words, tears that I thought were all used up. Emily is now 11 years old, and as I look at my beautiful, tall clever girl while I write, it seems like only yesterday she entered this world in a big hurry.

Photographs of Emily Molloy, Kevin Molloy, Ryan Molloy and Adam Molloy.

Emily, one week old

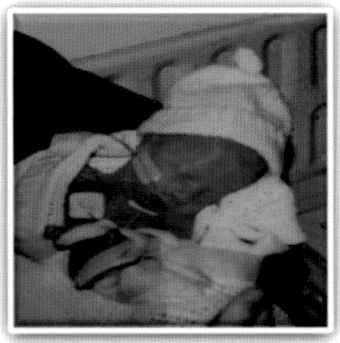

Ryan and Adam (on right), one week old

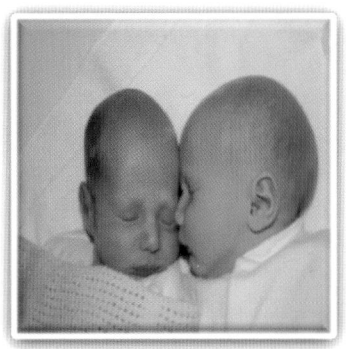

Kevin, one day old, with Emily, age five

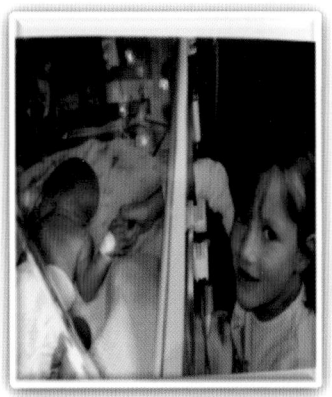

Emily, ten, Kevin, five and the twins, three weeks, with their grandad Paddy Molloy

⚳

Eva Smith Geraghty (26 weeks)

On the morning of 7 August, at 26 weeks into my pregnancy, my waters broke. We drove to Cavan General Hospital where they checked me over. The hospital decided to send me to Our Lady of Lourdes hospital in Drogheda, as they had the neonatal facilities for very preterm babies if needed. We headed to Drogheda Hospital, and I was given an injection to strengthen the baby's lungs. Doctors told us I would need complete bed rest and that the baby and I would be constantly monitored throughout the day.

My contractions started in earnest at about 8.30 p.m. At 10.30 p.m. the doctor examined me, and I was immediately rushed to the delivery room. Suddenly everything was happening very fast. My husband Francis and my mother rushed to be by my side, and after what seemed hours our little miracle Eva Smith Geraghty arrived. She was born on 8 August at 2.49 a.m. (and she even let out a little cry), weighing 0.74 kg (1 lb 8 oz). She was immediately taken away to the NICU. I think it was only when we saw her later in intensive care that we realised just how serious things were. Our beautiful fragile little one was lying on a hot bed, hooked up to all kinds of machines, so tiny and helpless. Little did we know how much we would learn about these machines and our baby's health in the months that were to follow.

During the night of Thursday, 10 August, I was woken up and told Eva was very ill and probably would not survive the night. We had to prepare ourselves to say goodbye, so Dad arrived and so did a priest, who baptised her. This was the longest night of our lives, but at about 6.00 a.m. the next morning Eva stabilised. Our little fighter made it through the night. That morning we met with Eva's paediatrician who explained that the hole in Eva's heart needed to be closed as it was affecting blood flow from the heart to the lungs. The previous night Eva's left lung had collapsed, she was still very ill and needed the surgery as soon as possible. The paediatrician warned us this was a very serious operation, especially for one as tiny as Eva, and that while she'd had patients who'd undergone it, they rarely survived.

At nine days old, Eva was taken by ambulance to Our Lady's Children's Hospital in Crumlin. She had her heart operation, which only took 45 minutes but they were the longest 45 minutes of our lives. Thankfully it was an absolute success. I remember the doctors and nurses commented on how good her colour was after the operation. Eva returned to Drogheda the following day and immediately began to come on in leaps and bounds. At 19 days, she came off ventilation. At 58 days, she again left Drogheda, this time for the NMH in Holles Street in Dublin. She had successful laser surgery on her eyes and even had her very first bottle-feed while there. A couple of days after returning to Drogheda, she came out of the incubator and was moved to special care. All these tiny steps which were gradually moving her closer to coming home. And finally, after 86 days in hospital, Eva came home.

When Eva arrived home, we were so nervous. We were given a respiration monitor to monitor her breathing in case she stopped. It took some of the fear of going home away. The staff had also told us not to hesitate in ringing the hospital at any time if we had any queries (which of course we did, and we were always treated in a caring and patient manner). Eva attended the hospital during the winter months to get the Synagis injection to protect her from the RSV infection (which can be very dangerous for premature babies). Apart from that, life began to return to normal.

As time went by we became more confident, life calmed down, and our baby reached all her milestones. Eva is now a very healthy, strong, energetic young girl. She has never looked back since the day she left hospital. She was discharged from the hospital aged three and only attends to see an eye specialist as she has a stigmatism on her eye. She loves animals, swimming, tennis and playing the piano. She became a big sister a year and a half ago to Naoise, a job she takes very seriously. She loves hearing the story of her life and knows just how special she is. Eva is our constant reminder that miracles do happen.

Photographs of Eva Smith Geraghty.

Eva and Mum, one day old

Eva at Christmas 2004

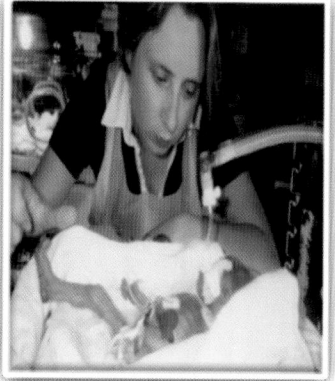

Eva, first day of school

Eva, Mum, Dad and sister Naoise on Eva's First Communion

Tiny Footprints

CR

Evan Byrne (29 weeks)

Evan was born on 29 September in the Mid-Western Regional Hospital, Limerick. It was an experience to be held forever in my mind. I was 29 weeks pregnant on my first baby, and then, out of the blue, at 2.00 a.m., whilst in bed at home, my waters broke. We went to the hospital to be told that the baby would arrive shortly. I was given steroid injections to help develop my baby's lungs. From this moment my mind went into overdrive. I had so many worries and questions swirling around in my mind. I had not heard much if anything about premature births. Would the baby survive? Would everything be OK? Then, at 10.10 p.m., our tiny little boy arrived into the world weighing 1.16 kg (2 lb 9 oz). It was all very emotional. The neonatal team rushed him away, and we waited what seemed like hours to hear if he was OK. The staff were amazing and gave us so much support during this time. When we saw Evan for the first time I was sick with nerves. He looked so tiny and helpless. He was all bruised, wires everywhere and on ventilation. It was an amazing feeling to finally get to hold my little boy a few days later, filled with emotion as I looked into his little face.

One of the hardest things was leaving our baby in hospital every day. All we had was the latest photo we had taken of him. It's very hard to express my feelings during this time to others. Words don't come easily to describe all the emotions we had. Those weeks spent in the neonatal unit were strange ones. Our baby and how he was doing became my priority. I focused all my energy on him, and he was all I could think about.

Evan did very well in the neonatal unit. He is a very strong-willed and brave boy, and I truly believe this helped him get through his hard start in life. After just six weeks of various ups and downs, with infections and numerous antibiotics, the day finally came when we were told we could take him home. I was filled with dread and excitement at this point. We had been waiting for this day but now so many 'what ifs' were running through my head. I was going to miss the comfort of having the nurses and doctors around.

The first year of Evan's life was tough-going for us. I was paranoid about cleanliness and afraid of leaving him with anyone. He had numerous infections and had to stay in hospital. He suffered with gastroesophageal reflux and was admitted to hospital and put on a prescription formula to try to help him gain weight as he just kept vomiting after every feed. This caused a lot of discomfort for him which meant he would cry a lot, but we got there in the end with a bit of trial and error. There was a meningitis scare when he was about six months old, but thankfully this turned out to be a viral infection, and after a few more viral infections in year one, all has turned out OK. Today, apart from the scars on his hands, you would never know about the tough journey he had at the start of his life. We are so blessed to have this little boy, who is doing so well, and who we love more than anything. He is just the funniest little man and brings so much joy to us all.

Photographs of Evan Byrne.

Evan, two weeks old

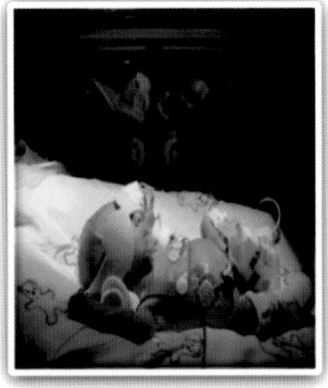

Evan, six months old

Evan, 21 months old

Evan, three years old

Evan Harrington and Killian Harrington (30 weeks)

When my husband Clem and I got married, we never thought we would have problems having little ones. However, when we decided to try for a family, it just did not happen for us. One miscarriage, and, honestly, we had given up hope. Just as we had begun the route of investigating what our conceiving issues were, we discovered we were expecting not just one but two babies. The excitement, nervousness and anticipation were unbelievable. In early December, at nearly 30 weeks, I had back pains and thought it was a kidney infection. Little did we know. At around 1.00 a.m. we rang the maternity ward, and they told us to come in. So off we went with only my handbag. When we got there, I was told I was in labour, but the doctors said they would try to stop it. We were relieved when we heard this, but it was too late, an emergency section was needed.

Killian was born first, followed by Evan, on 8 December, weighing 1.39 kg (3 lb 1 oz) each, but there was silence in the room. No cries, only the sound of the neonatal staff trying to get our two little boys to breathe. I couldn't see what was going on, but Clem could. To this day he finds it hard to watch medical emergency programmes on television. It just brings back so many vivid memories. Clem went with the boys to the NICU where they were both ventilated upon arrival. When I got to see them later that day I was shocked. We couldn't believe they were ours. We couldn't hold them as they were not stable enough. It was two days before I got to hold Killian and 10 days before I got to hold Evan. Not holding them did not prevent me from bonding with them at all. I knew that they were safe in their incubator, and I couldn't be selfish trying to hold them. I expressed my milk; it was my way to be close to them. It was the only thing I felt I could do for them. One of the hardest parts was leaving the hospital and the boys behind. The guilt, the worry and the fear of the unknown ahead.

Every morning Clem went to NICU to check the boys. He dreaded going in, not knowing what to expect or what he would see. By 10.00 a.m. every morning I would be there and would spend the day talking, singing, looking at and touching them through the little doors in the incubators. It was a tense time, waiting for the boys to be taken off breathing ventilators, to start on CPAP and begin their tube-feeds. Then we were faced with a few setbacks such as when they got an infection and had to temporarily stop feeds; it felt like two steps back, one step forward.

On Christmas Eve, the NICU was very busy, and this day was to become the longest day ever for us. One baby would stop breathing, and then the other kept forgetting to breathe. It was hard listening to the alarms constantly going off. They seemed to settle down that evening, and we were told to go home. We got absolutely no sleep that night. We were in the unit by 8.00 a.m. on Christmas morning to make sure our little boys were OK, and they were. They had just wanted to give us a fright. On New Year's Day, Evan had a blood transfusion. His little head was shaved to put in the shunt, and he looked so sick. There were a lot of tears that day, but it gave him the boost that he needed. Two weeks later our two boys were moved to cots – progress at last. The boys then moved on to independent feeding of expressed milk. Shortly afterwards we were told we could take Evan home. We were so happy but so sad at the same time, as we had to leave Killian behind.

On our first night at home, we stayed up all night with Evan, panicked at 3.00 a.m. and ended up with my mum and sister in my house as I was afraid that he was going to stop breathing. Two days later, Killian came home. It was so exciting, there were no tears that day, as both boys would be at home. No one had seen the boys except for grandparents. And then the busy work began: no sleep, worries, hospital appointments, afraid to take them out and no one to the house in case they got an infection . . . it was unreal. Then they attained their milestones, getting to 3.18 kg (7 lb), their first trip out in a buggy, their christenings, everyone meeting them. Killian and Evan will be starting school on 1 September. They have become two big boys with no problems or after-effects of being premature. We count ourselves so lucky every day to have two beautiful little boys, and a little girl Abigail, who arrived 18 months after them.

Photographs of Evan Harrington and Killian Harrington.

Evan, day 4

Killian, day 4

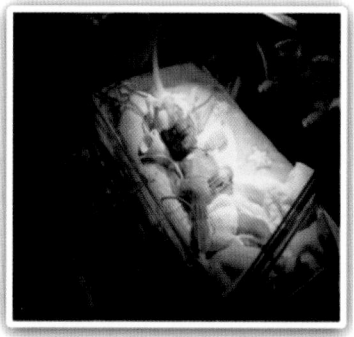
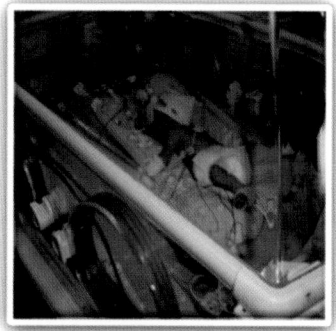

Evan and Killian with Daddy, aged four months

Evan and Killian aged four, with Abigail aged three

CR

Evan Prendergast (29 weeks)

Our family was blessed with a little miracle: Evan Prendergast. Our little miracle has overcome all odds and has to this day lived up to his name, Evan, meaning 'little warrior'. At 29 weeks, following a very complicated pregnancy, Evan was born on 24 June, weighing 1.38 kg (3 lb). Following a haemorrhage at 18 weeks of pregnancy, it was discovered I had a placental haematoma, which meant that the placenta was coming away from the wall of the womb. Blood flow to the baby was compromised, and no one was sure to what extent. We were uncertain whether baby Evan would hold on until 24 weeks to give him any chance of survival. The next few weeks were filled with emergency trips to the hospital, each time thinking we were losing our baby. When I reached 24 weeks, I was hospitalised for the remainder of the pregnancy. It was then discovered I had a clot in the iliac vein in my right leg, causing further medical complications. I was unable to take anticoagulants while pregnant and haemorrhaging; therefore I had an inferior-vena-cava filter inserted under MRI in St James's Hospital, Dublin. The filter was inserted into the inferior vena cava, one of the body's large veins, to prevent the clot from travelling to my heart and lungs, possibly causing a fatal pulmonary embolism. Due to continued haemorrhaging, it was a dilemma for the doctors as to whether it was better for the baby to be delivered or not. I was under constant supervision, not knowing if our baby was to be born that night or the next. We hoped and prayed that Evan would hang on for as long as possible.

Thankfully he did, but I suffered from a placental rupture at 29 weeks. Luckily, I was in the Coombe Women and Infants University Hospital in Dublin, and Evan was born safely by

Tiny Footprints

emergency Caesarean section, stunning everyone in the theatre with his cries! He was immediately whisked away to NICU in an incubator. Unfortunately I also ended up in intensive care following further complications during the C-section. As I was in ICU, I did not see Evan for three days. It was a tough time; however, Evan was doing well, only requiring CPAP for four days before being able to breathe unaided.

Eventually I got to see Evan, and so started our new life of NICU visits, doctors' rounds, breast pumps, EBM, tube-feeding and kangaroo care. At first we were like deer caught in the headlights, but we quickly got used to the routine of NICU. At 1.38 kg (3 lb), Evan struggled to maintain his weight. However, after three weeks, he started to gain weight and began to thrive. He was moved from NICU to the SCBU, and two weeks later he was homeward bound at only 1.8 kg (4 lb).

While we were delighted to have our baby home to meet his big sister, Evan still had a lot to go through. He had a hernia operation and a cyst under his arm which was a side effect of the BCG vaccination. There were Synagis injections against the RSV virus, physiotherapy appointments, developmentals and check-ups galore. One year on, and Evan is a very smiley, mischievous little boy, who is now taking his first steps. He amazes us all. He is our little warrior.

Photographs of Evan Prendergast.

Evan, six hours old   *Evan with his mammy*

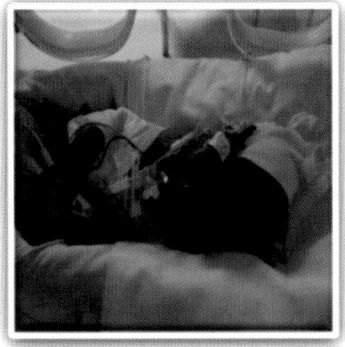

Evan with his sister Alannah *Evan, one year old*

Eve Myron (27 weeks)

On 15 December, at a routine check-up, I was transferred by ambulance from Wexford General Hospital to the Rotunda Hospital in Dublin after being told that my baby was arriving early. I was give steroid injections to help the baby's lungs to mature, and at 9.53 p.m. on Monday, 21 December, at 27 weeks' gestation, Eve decided to make her swift appearance into the world. My husband TJ wasn't there for her birth as our son Glen was appearing in his first school play, and he only got the message after the performance. Luckily I had my friend Heather there for support, and she was great.

When Eve was born, she cried, and after a quick kiss she was taken to the NICU for examination. By the time TJ had driven up from home in freezing conditions, we were allowed in to see her. She was so small and transparent, weighing just 0.94 kg (2 lb 1 oz). She was ventilated that first night, and the following morning she was put on CPAP. On her first day her incubator was filled with vapour. This was to help her skin acclimatise to the outside world. Eve was two days old when I got to hold her for the first time. I was terrified as she was so fragile and I was afraid of hurting her. I came home on Christmas Eve just in time for Santa, and he even remembered to leave presents for Eve.

Eve was breathing on her own for 13 hours a day by the end of her first week, but then started to have decelerations. This was a very worrying time; she was struggling with her oxygen levels, her skin was blotchy, and she looked very unwell. Some days she couldn't come off CPAP at all. All the wires and monitors were very scary, but we got used to them. However, we never got used to the panic we felt when Eve was having a bradycardia. This was extremely difficult as she would change to a grey colour, her heart rate would drop very low, and she would have to be stimulated to remind her to breathe. These episodes stopped after she got a top-up of blood via transfusion in early January. All in all, she was on CPAP for 47 days. I travelled up from home on snow-filled roads (130 miles round trip), just to get a glimpse of her and bring her feeds; thinking back now, the roads were extremely bad but it is amazing what you do under these circumstances.

Eve reached 1.36 kg (3 lb) on 23 January, 35 days after she was born, and things seemed to move very quickly after that. She was wearing clothes, maintaining her own temperature, taking her feeds and even lifting her head. I remember buying some 1.81 kg (4 lb) vests. They were the size of a bib and they were still too big for her, but she was wearing clothes and I had washing to do, which was very important for me. On 8 February she graduated to a cot. In the meantime, Glen was going to school and was being looked after by my parents and family in Dublin.

On 11 February, seven weeks after she came into the world, Eve was transferred to Wexford General Hospital, weighing 1.9 kg (4 lb 3 oz). It was hard to leave the staff and hospital who had helped Eve so much, but so great to be getting closer to home. I waited in Wexford, the thought of my tiny little girl travelling by ambulance almost unbelievable. She had gone through so much and still shouldn't have been born for another six weeks. However, it was so much easier to visit when she was in Wexford. I could now see her daily while my pal Hazel looked after Glen.

Eve was thriving and came home on 20 February. I stayed with her the night before she came home so we could get used to each other. Glen really couldn't wait to see his little sister, he was so excited. Eve settled in easily at home, and I was very comfortable with her. I thought that I would be nervous, but now it was my chance to make up for all the cuddles we missed out on in her earlier days. It was great to hold her without watching monitors! Eve is a beautiful 19-month-old now, who enjoys life to the full and has met all her milestones. We are very proud of our little girl. We could never thank enough the doctors and nurses, who helped our little girl come home safe to us, or our families and friends for all their help and support. We couldn't have come through this difficult time without them.

Photographs of Eve Myron.

Eve, almost a big 3 lb

Eve, seven days old

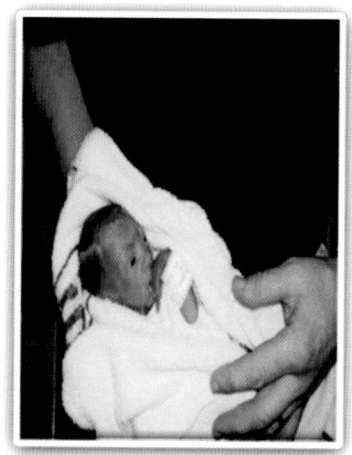

Big brother Glen gets his first cuddle

Eve at 18 months

Farah Ammara (33 weeks) and Jena Ammara (28 weeks)

My name is Michelle, and this is my story to motherhood. Due to severe pre-eclampsia, my first daughter Farah was born on 9 March at almost 33 weeks, weighing 1.42 kg (3 lb 2 oz). We had never seen anyone so small, and both my husband and I were so scared for our daughter. Luckily, as it turned out, even though she was so small for her dates she was very strong and only spent three weeks in hospital. The day we brought her home was one of the happiest days of our lives, and since then she has gone from strength to strength.

When I realised I was pregnant again in the following summer, naturally we were delighted but also very concerned because of what had happened in my previous pregnancy. At week 20 my fears were confirmed when, at a regular check-up, it was revealed that my blood pressure was elevated. I was immediately given medication to control it, but by week 27 I had to be hospitalised as my blood pressure was too high. While in hospital it became obvious that I wouldn't go to term with this pregnancy as my placenta was not supporting the baby sufficiently, and on the morning of 21 January it was decided that our baby would be delivered. We were terrified and couldn't believe it was happening so soon. Our daughter Jena was born that afternoon weighing just 0.88 kg (1 lb 15 oz). Jena spent the first five days of her life on CPAP, but on day 6 it was decided to ventilate her so that she would have more energy to fight an infection in her gut. She spent the next seven days on a ventilator, and on the day before she was due to come off it she decided in the middle of the night she had had enough and pulled it out herself. From then on she had some intermittent feeding problems but by week 4 she had turned a corner and left the NICU. By week 7 she was off all oxygen, and it was just a matter of feeding and growing. Jena took her bottle for the first time on her due date, which was 11 April, and came home four days later, exactly 12 weeks to the day after she was born.

Photographs of Farah Ammara and Jena Ammara.

Farah, almost two months old

Jena, two months old

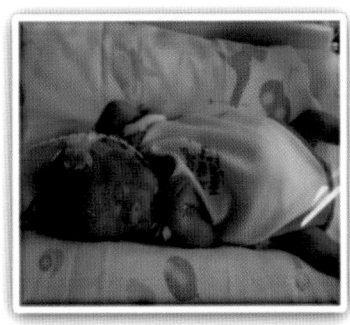

Big sister Farah, aged two, with Jena

Sisterly love, Jena at four months

‱

Finn Doyle (28 weeks)

Finn was born on 2 October by emergency Caesarean section at 28 weeks' gestation, weighing just 1.05 kg (2 lb 5 oz). There seemed to be no apparent reason as to why Finn came so early. My waters broke the day before, so the decision was made to deliver to prevent any infection. When he was born, Finn started to cry, which was such a relief to hear. It meant he had a fighting chance. I got to see him for just one minute before he was taken away, and an hour later, when he had been stabilised, his daddy got to see him. The NICU in the hospital where Finn was born was full, so he was transferred to another hospital in Dublin four hours later. I remember the nurse bringing him to say goodbye before he embarked on his big journey, and all I could see were these little eyes peeping out at me from under a blue-and-yellow knitted hat. We had a few moments together before he was taken in the ambulance to the other hospital. His daddy followed him to make sure he got settled in OK, but it was the next day before I was strong enough to see him. It was such a frightening experience when I first walked into the NICU. I didn't know where Finn was, and there were so many incubators and alarms going off. Luckily his daddy knew which incubator was his and had even met some of the medical staff the night before. The nurses had put a card on the front of his incubator which read, 'Hello my name is Finn.' It was so cute and really made me smile, even though I was terrified. Finn was wide awake, with those little eyes peeping out at me once again, but this time I was able to reach in and touch him, and he squeezed my finger.

The first few hours and days were critical. We were constantly looking at our phones, waiting for a call, but, thank

God, Finn was a fighter and we never received any calls. By day 3 he was hungry and stable and ready for food, so I started expressing breastmilk to give him. Finn spent his first few days of life on a ventilator but soon became strong enough to move to CPAP. It was a full week later before he was stable enough for me to hold, and we got to do kangaroo care, which was amazing. It was such a wonderful experience to hold my tiny baby so close to me. Finn was baptised when he was two weeks old by the hospital chaplain, Anne. She had already blessed him and had done a lovely prayer for him, but we wanted to do anything and everything we could to help him thrive. It was a lovely ceremony, and Finn's grandparents were allowed into the NICU to take part. It seemed that all our hopes and prayers were beginning to work, as day by day Finn's weight and strength grew.

During his time in the NICU Finn received three blood transfusions to help boost his blood oxygen levels. It was amazing to see how each transfusion made him stronger. A lovely pink-coloured baby with lots of energy, who was constantly trying to pull his CPAP off. By week 7, Finn was ready to come off CPAP and go on just a trickle of oxygen. He also moved into a cot and out of the high-dependency section of the NICU, which meant I could bottle-feed and hold him every day. Finn loved being in the cot and really enjoyed the freedom of not being in an incubator. He would lie there smiling out at me. Soon enough he was on the road to home, and the nurses showed us how to bathe and change him. Finn left hospital on 18 December, weighing 3.4 kg (7 lb 8 oz), and the whole family were so excited to meet the little boy they had heard so much about.

Finn soon settled into his new home, and as the weeks went by, he just kept growing and growing. By the summer he was starting to sit, and then he was crawling. Soon after Christmas he started to walk and then run. Finn is now nearing his second birthday, and we are so lucky that he has not had one health problem and that he has caught up to his corrected age. He is now a happy, lively boy who is full of fun and does not sit still for a minute. Finn is a fighter who never gave up and was an inspiration to my husband and me. He fought such a tough battle: we love you, Finn, and are so proud of you.

Photographs of Finn Doyle.

Finn, day 1, first touch for
Mammy

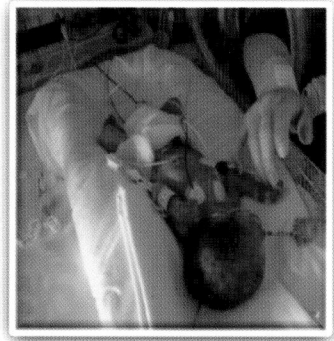

Finn, three weeks old,
kangaroo care with Mammy

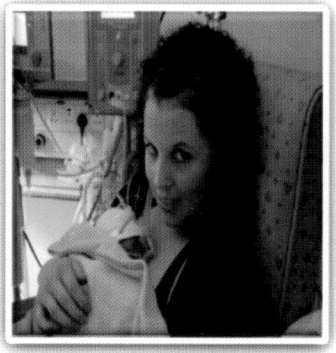

Finn, six weeks old

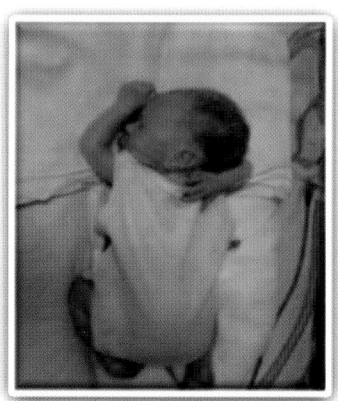

Finn, 18 months old with
Mammy and Daddy

Freya McEntaggart and Seán McEntaggart (28 weeks)

After two failed IUI fertility treatments, we were third time lucky when in February we found out we were expecting. When the shock of finally getting pregnant started to settle in, we were given another surprise when at eight weeks we found out we were expecting not one but two babies. On 4 August we were given the biggest shock of all when, at just 28 weeks, I went into labour. At 1.36 p.m., baby Freya was born by emergency Caesarean weighing just 0.89 kg (1 lb 15 oz). She was closely followed by her brother Seán, who was born at 1.38 p.m., weighing just 0.9 kg (1 lb 15 oz). It was a day of joy, excitement, fear and worry.

I got to see my babies the following day. The sight of my two precious yet tiny babies hooked up to ventilators, monitors and IV drips was terrifying. We had no idea what the next 12 weeks in NICU had in store for us. I was lucky enough to have such a supportive family who were there for us when we were scared on the bad days and who laughed and smiled with us on the good days. The first few days were scary. Seán was born with a grade-2 bleed on the brain, fluid on his lungs and a PDA, and he was also finding it hard to tolerate his feeds. It was three weeks later when I finally got to hold my tiny baby boy. He was so small and fragile but a strong little man all the same. He was on and off ventilators for seven weeks before he went on to the oxygen nasal prongs. Each time he came off his CPAP machine for a few minutes longer we could see he was getting stronger.

We got to hold Freya three days after she was born. I was terrified holding my little girl. She was also so small and delicate. Holding her close to me gave me great strength and courage. I knew I had to be strong for Freya and her brother. Freya spent her first seven weeks fighting infections and trying to tolerate her feeds. She also had a PDA and took three courses of medication before it closed up for her. She came off her CPAP at about eight weeks after fighting with the nurses every time they fixed her mask after she pulled it off. She then started slowly taking bottle-feeds from nine weeks.

At seven weeks Freya and Seán were moved a step up and put into their very own cots. Such a feeling of happiness we had when we walked in to find our babies no longer covered up in big scary incubators. They spent two weeks in the low-dependency unit before getting moved to the wing for a further three weeks. It was great getting to spend all day caring for both Freya and Seán. We were beginning to feel like proper parents at last. We got to feed, change and bath them whenever we liked. We no longer had to worry about tubes and wires.

The five weeks after ICU were spent getting the twins off the oxygen and onto the bottle-feeds. At 11 weeks we finally got to hold our two babies together after they decided to come off the oxygen together. Every day we arrived to find more and more positive things were happening. On 26 October we got the long-awaited news: we were finally getting our babies home the following day. This day coincidentally happened to be their due date.

We had spent the past 12 weeks getting the nursery ready, gathering up all the baby essentials and preparing ourselves for the two new little people who were about to change our lives in a whole new different but wonderful way. Four weeks after getting Freya and Seán home, Seán had to go to Temple Street Children's University Hospital in Dublin to have an operation to repair an inguinal hernia. Seán spent five days in intensive care as his prematurity compromised his ability to tolerate the anaesthetic.

Freya and Seán are just about to turn one, and both babies are thriving and always full of big smiles. Freya has turned out to be the bossy baby who likes to keep us busy whereas Seán is the quiet, laid-back baby who soaks up everything going on around him. Put them together and they are two joyful characters with whom we have been truly blessed. They are two little miracles who have taught us to never give up and to always believe and have strength.

Photographs of Seán McEntaggart and Freya McEntaggart.

Freya, Day 1

Seán, Day 3

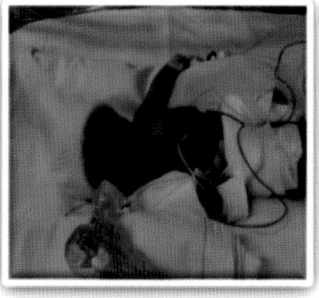
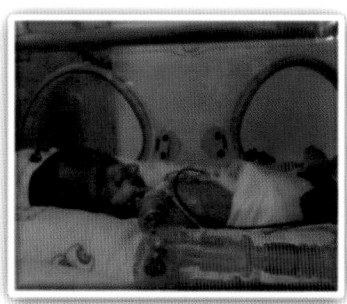

Freya and Seán at Christmas

Seán and Freya

Gabrielle Dodog and Michael Dodog (26 weeks)

When our first son was almost a year old, we decided we wanted to have another baby. My first pregnancy was full term, and there were no complications, so we presumed the second one would be the same. We couldn't have been more mistaken. My first scan showed that we were having twins. The doctor told us it was a high-risk pregnancy. We were a little scared, but excited at the same time. My pregnancy progressed well, other than the usual symptoms and extreme tiredness. At 25 weeks and 6 days' gestation, I started feeling pain in my lower abdomen. I went to my doctor who told me it was an infection and I was prescribed antibiotics. However, the next day the pain was so bad I had to go to the hospital. Within minutes of arriving at the hospital I found out I was in labour. I couldn't believe what was happening. I was given medication to try to stop my labour but it only delayed it for several hours. At 26 weeks and 1 day I had our twins: a son weighing 1.04 kg (2 lb 4 oz) and a daughter weighing 0.84 kg (1 lb 14 oz).

The babies were taken straight to the NICU. We decided to call them after two angels, Michael and Gabrielle, for extra help. When I saw them for the first time it was so emotional, my two little babies wrapped in wires, with tubes all around, it was heartbreaking. The medical team told us that there was a problem with Gabrielle. There was air in her abdomen where her feeding tube had perforated her stomach. She needed to be transferred from Cork to Dublin for further investigation. All I remember is hearing the nurse telling us that a priest was on the way and that we could christen our babies. I looked at my husband, speechless, and in total shock, but he reassured me that everything was going to be fine.

After reaching the hospital in Dublin, we asked the doctors what our little girl's chances of survival were. At that point we were told it was 50–50. We cried so much leaving her in Dublin, but we needed to get back to Michael. Gabrielle was brought to theatre the following day. She recovered really well after the surgery and was back in Cork within three days. We were so happy and relieved. We were really worried about her because she was much smaller than her brother.

Michael was ventilated for a few hours after birth before being put onto CPAP. On the seventh day he developed a very serious life-threatening intestinal infection called NEC. He had to be fully ventilated at that point. We found it hard to believe what was happening. We learnt that you can only take one day at a time with a premature baby. Michael was so unwell, even the smallest change of position caused him to stop breathing. A few days after he contracted NEC, I got a phone call from the hospital telling me that Michael's bowel had perforated and he needed to be transferred to Dublin. We assumed because he was bigger than his sister that he would be stronger. However, when the doctors examined him they were not sure if he would survive. He needed to have few centimetres of bowel removed and a stoma put in. A blood culture then revealed he had *E. coli*. Michael was put back into the NICU. A few days later we received more bad news. He also needed to have heart surgery for a PDA. I just could not bear to see my little baby endure so much. Thankfully, his surgeries went well. His stoma was slow to work but eventually things began to improve. After three weeks in Our Lady's Children's Hospital in Crumlin, Michael was transferred back to Cork University Maternity Hospital.

We were so happy having our two babies together. Gabrielle at this point was doing well, but then she was diagnosed with a grade-2 bleed on the brain, and she developed breathing problems. However, within a few days the twins were transferred out of intensive care. Michael came off CPAP, but Gabrielle developed a long-term lung condition called CLD. She also needed the same heart surgery as her brother, so she was slower to breathe on her own. Michael had to go for further surgery in Dublin, but after 104 days in hospital he was eventually discharged. Gabrielle spent a little less: 91 days. They are now one year old. We have one more surgery to undergo and hopefully that is it. Our babies and our experience have changed our life completely. We have learnt to appreciate life so much more now after everything we have all been through.

Photographs of Gabrielle Dodog and Michael Dodog.

Michael, 15 hours old

Gabrielle, 15 hours old

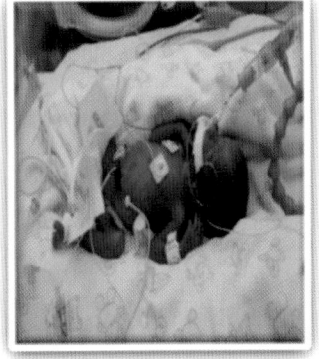
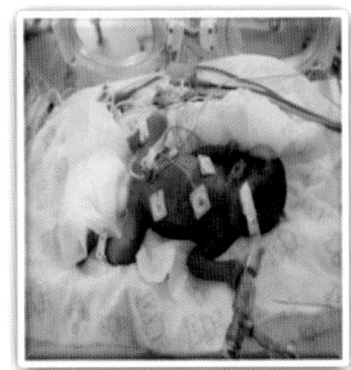

Michael and Gabrielle

Michael and Gabrielle today

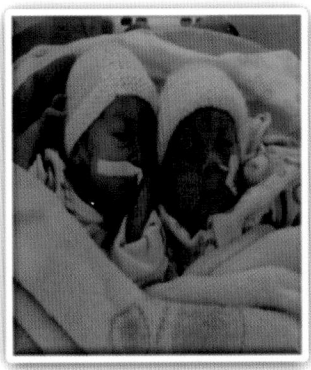

❧

Harris Lawless (rest in peace) (32 weeks), Ayeisha Lawless (32 weeks) and Kameron Lawless (26 weeks)

When I was 21, I got an unexpected surprise when I found out I was pregnant. My son was due the first week of August, although I knew he had to be delivered at 38 weeks' gestation. I had sailed through the pregnancy until the beginning of May when I started to suffer problems with my heart. I was born with hypertrophic obstructive cardiomyopathy – or sudden death syndrome as it is more commonly known. I began to struggle with every normal task, and breathing was becoming a major problem for me. The doctors had assured me that despite my medical issues my baby was fine.

One day in May I could not feel the baby's movements. I went to hospital to see what the problem was, and I was hospitalised for monitoring. I was released the following day and was assured that my baby was doing fine. The following week I was at the hospital for a routine outpatient appointment. I was told the news that no mother should have to get, I was told my baby had died in the womb. I was one day off 32 weeks in my pregnancy. A week later, I was induced and gave birth naturally to my little beautiful boy, Harris. He was 1.5 kg (3 lb 5 oz). It was only after my son's death that the doctors realised he had starved in the womb due to a restriction of blood flow, as my heart was not strong enough for both of us.

The medical team advised me not to have any more children as it would be too dangerous. Four months later I underwent heart surgery and had a defibrillator implanted as it was not known at the time but my heart was too weak to cope with natural childbirth.

A year later, I found out I was expecting again, a little baby girl. The doctors were more aware of the dangers this time around. I was put on beta blockers to keep my heart as normal as possible although I was warned that they do reduce the birth weight of the baby. (I was put on beta blockers a week before my son's death, and in my mind they played a contributory factor in his death. I know now that this was not the case, but I needed something or someone to blame for his death.) I was monitored on a weekly basis. At week 32, my daughter was not getting the nutrients she needed to survive. She was delivered and weighed 1.53 kg (3 lb 6 oz). Ayeisha was kept in the SCBU for 18 days, and she was released with no problems. She is a healthy and happy two-and-a-half-year-old at the time of writing this.

When my daughter was just 11 months old, I discovered I was pregnant for the third time. It was the most frightening time of our lives. Doctors asked me to consider a termination of the pregnancy as under no circumstances would my heart be strong enough to go through another pregnancy. I refused, especially once I had seen the heartbeat and knew that there was a tiny life depending on me. I had to give them a chance. I was warned by the medical staff that death could be a possibility for me, and as a worst-case scenario neither of us would survive. I was still adamant that I was not taking their advice. I was closely monitored, and at 22 weeks it was noticed that there was a restriction of blood flow to the baby. I was immediately hospitalised, and I was given four doses of steroids to help with the development of the baby's lungs in case he had to be delivered.

At 26 weeks and 2 days, my little champ was born. Kameron was ventilated for nine hours and then put on CPAP for 43 days. He was on oxygen until day 103. The doctors resorted to giving him diuretics to get him off the oxygen.

Kameron was also born with two spots on the brain, a large PDA, moderate PFO reflux, a hernia and sleep apnoea. When he eventually came home in November 2010 he was discharged with a respiratory monitor. Despite getting the Synagis injections to protect him against the RSV, he contracted this infection in January 2011 and was admitted to hospital with a collapsed lung. He was released home in February. For the last five months he has been hospitalised six times with pneumonia and other breathing difficulties. He has severe CLD now. He fights every illness, and thankfully comes out smiling each time. It just shows you that miracles can happen, and this little man is one in a million.

Photographs of Ayeisha Lawless and Kameron Lawless.

Ayeisha, 18 months old

Kameron, a few hours old

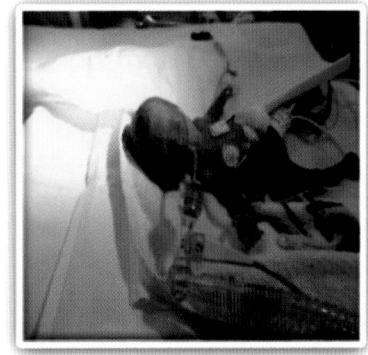

Kameron, one month old

Kameron, one year old

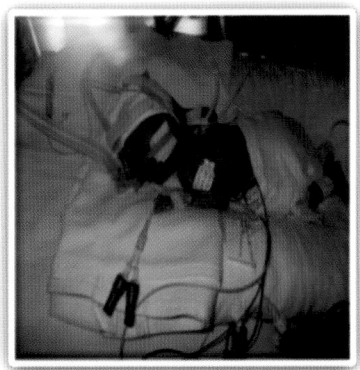

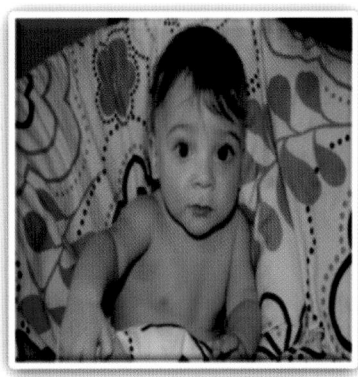

CR

Harry Lee (26 weeks)

Because I had developed toxaemia, our little boy Harry arrived 16 weeks early, on 16 January, via emergency Caesarean section. The blood flow through the umbilical cord had reversed, and we were both in danger of losing our lives. Harry was born weighing 0.61 kg (1 lb 6 oz). He was so small, barely a handful. We were told that he might not make it through the first 72 hours and that they only see babies as sick as Harry once or twice a year. His prognosis didn't look good.

The first hurdle with Harry, apart from his extremely low birth weight and respiratory distress, was his having poor perfusion (circulation of blood) to his right leg. His big toe turned black, and the initial fear was that, if he survived, he would lose his leg. However, the circulation returned spontaneously, and within a week the black toe turned pink. At two weeks of age Harry contracted NEC, which caused his whole body to swell. This caused extremely low blood pressure and required numerous blood transfusions. There was a chance that Harry's bowel might perforate, which could be fatal, but thankfully he fought off the infection and slowly recovered. However, he then developed a grade-2 bleed as a result of the infection. He also had PDA which had opened wider from the pressure of the NEC on his tiny body.

At four weeks of age Harry was well enough to have his first cuddle with me. It was an amazing feeling to see him so close. At five weeks, he went into respiratory distress and stopped breathing for 17 minutes. This is known as bronchopulmonary dysplasia, and it caused Harry's lungs to seize up, resulting in apnoea. The nurses and doctors kept oxygen circulating in his body in order not to starve his brain.

Thankfully after a few days it seemed to settle. Harry had at this stage been ventilated from birth. After a long six weeks, Harry finally cuddled his daddy, who didn't want to let him go.

At six weeks, Harry was struck down with another infection, and we were called to the hospital in the middle of the night and told to prepare ourselves for the worst. Harry's lungs had collapsed, and he was on full life support. If he didn't start fighting himself then we were going to lose him. We sat by his incubator willing him to fight. They had to sedate him to try and let his body heal. Watching him so lifeless was heartbreaking. Five days after the initial diagnosis, by some miracle, or just pure strength, Harry started to improve slightly. After two weeks the pneumonia had gone and we were on the road to recovery again. Harry had now been diagnosed with CLD and continued to be ventilated.

As the days went on, we were very anxious that Harry was still ventilated. His lungs were so weak. He was sent to Our Lady's Children's Hospital in Crumlin to have a bronchoscopy to inspect his trachea for any structural abnormalities. Thankfully, in the absence of any abnormalities, he progressed to CPAP after 12 weeks on ventilation. One week later he was big enough to be moved to a cot. We could finally touch and cuddle him when we wanted.

Four more weeks went by with us watching Harry grow and get stronger although we were still anxious that he wasn't quite ready to go home. Harry developed zone 3 ROP in his eyes and required laser surgery. We knew that the odds of the surgery working were very good, but our fear was that he would have to be ventilated again. Thankfully the surgery went well, and Harry recovered and was taken back off the ventilator that day. One week later, I walked into Harry's room to find him on nasal prongs and being bottle-fed. He was finally on his way home. Two weeks later, on 1 June, our brave little hero came home. Harry is home on a small amount of oxygen support and should be off it by October.

From the moment I was told that they had to deliver Harry early, we were told that he might have disabilities and learning difficulties and that he might not even survive. Then he came into the world, and he got everything that they said he would. He seemed to get every infection possible. We were told so many times that Harry might not make it, yet he proved everybody wrong. He was never going anywhere but home with his mammy and daddy. We are so proud of Harry and the amazing journey he has brought us all on. We wouldn't change a thing about how Harry came into the world. It has made him the strong little boy that he is today.

Photographs of Harry Lee.

Harry, four days old

Harry, 10 weeks old

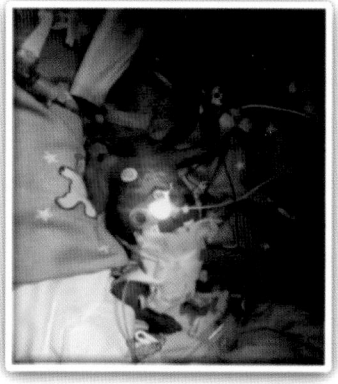
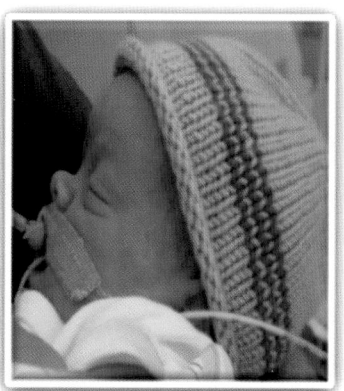

Harry, 15 weeks old

Harry, 25 weeks old

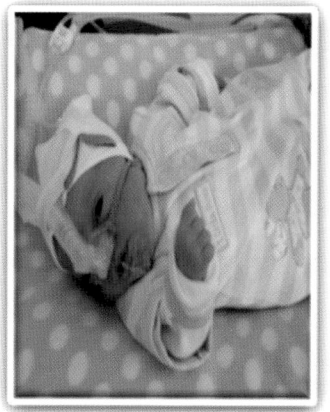

Holly Kelly (27 weeks)

Looking at my happy, feisty two-year-old now, you would never imagine the fight she had to put in to get where she is today. Due to complications during pregnancy and after a long stay in hospital, Holly made her appearance to the world 13 weeks early, at the NMH in Dublin, weighing 0.65 kg (1 lb 7 oz), ever so tiny.

We caught a quick glance of her before she was whisked away to the NICU. Nobody knew the road that lay ahead of us. Due to being confined to the bed, it was 24 hours before I got to see Holly, maybe the longest 24 hours of my life. Nobody can prepare you for seeing your tiny baby hooked up to (what I believed to be) every wire tube and monitor available, and you can't help thinking how such a tiny person, with the ability to fit into the palm of your hand, can fight on. The first few days I was in hospital with her consisted of me and my partner Karl staring in at her and trying to figure out who she looked like, any flicker of a hand or foot had us amazed, and any beep of a monitor made our hearts pound.

Every day was a roller-coaster ride, from chest drains, a heart murmur, jaundice, blood transfusions, CLD and several infections. Holly fought them all, with the same determination she has today. The day I went home and had to leave my tiny baby was tough. I felt my heart break. Every visit was different. One day we would have her out for a cuddle, her placed down our tops for skin-to-skin care, and we would sit for hours just savouring every minute. The next day she might have an infection, so we could only chat through the opening of the incubator. Holly stayed on high-frequency ventilation for three days. She then went onto CPAP, but within a week she slowly came off and moved to special care.

When Holly was three weeks old, doctors at Holles Street were happy with her progress and arranged for her transfer to Our Lady of Lourdes Hospital in Drogheda. Unfortunately she took the journey badly, and she quickly went back to square one. That was a very hard day. It was difficult when I thought back to the week before, when Holly was not hooked up to those dreaded beeping monitors, and then after the transfer she was back in intensive care. Her returning to being extremely vulnerable hit us hard.

We watched her weight like hawks because we knew that if she could just build her weight up her ability to fight off whatever came her way would be stronger. And we were there for every feed and rang every evening for her weight progress. Every ounce was a bonus. There are very special moments that will stay with me for ever such as her first nappy change and my first cuddle to her first bottle, her first babygro, her first bath; I could go on and on. Each one a milestone in her long road. Her progress from intensive care to special care to the room preparing you for home – every move was a day to remember. We had heard all the worst possible outcomes for premature babies, especially ones as young and as tiny as Holly, but thankfully, three months later, after spending her time in NICU, on her actual due date of 28 October she was allowed come home. The excitement that day was electric, our miracle baby home against the odds.

Family and friends would say how small she was, but I thought she was enormous. She seemed to thrive at home, getting bigger and bigger. We brought Holly for her weekly check-ups and she received her monthly Synagis injections to protect her against the RSV infection, which is particularly dangerous to premature babies. Then, all of a sudden, the calendar was blank and we had our girl all to ourselves. And though it took her a little longer to reach her milestones, she still reached them.

Holly is now a happy, healthy two-year-old. She is a girly girl without a doubt, loving anything pink, frilly or glittery. She has favourite TV programmes and sings me songs from them on a daily basis. She is my companion on shopping trips and outings and has developed a circle of friends. She still has a couple of issues regarding her eyes and weight, but these are minor compared to what might have been. Every day I am thankful for her. She amazes me still today, filling my life with happiness, pride and laughter. My precious daughter, my little fighter.

Photographs of Holly Kelly.

Holly, two days old, weighing 0.72 kg

Holly, three months old

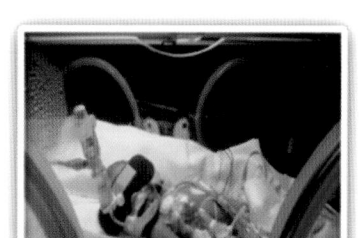

Holly, 13 months old

Holly, 20 months old

Jack Falbo (31 weeks)

When Jack was born at 31 weeks and 5 days, on Thursday, 11 October, weighing 1.84 kg (4 lb 1 oz), I didn't know what to think. A few months earlier we were delighted to find out we were finally expecting. We had been trying for three years on our own but hadn't been successful so we had turned to fertility treatment. This was our last month of treatment. We were so excited.

My pregnancy was very difficult. I was in and out of hospital with morning sickness, pains and low blood pressure. I started to feel better around 20 weeks and began to tell people about my pregnancy. Little did I know at that time that it wasn't going to be long until the end of my pregnancy. I went into early labour, at 26 weeks, but thankfully the doctors managed to stop the labour. As a precaution I was given steroids to develop the baby's lungs. At the time we were given very little information about the risks involved.

Five weeks later, despite the doctors' best effort to delay his arrival, Jack was born. He was transferred to the NICU, and my husband went with him. I was left alone with the obstetrician. I felt so alone, and this would be the overriding emotion over the following few months. I found it extremely difficult to have relatives and friends visiting me as I didn't have a baby to show them and we had little information on Jack's condition. Over the next three days, Jack's condition deteriorated. Doctors had discovered that his lungs, bowels and stomach weren't developed. The NICU didn't have the equipment needed to cater for the extent of his health problems and he needed to be transferred to a more specialised ICU. Finding a hospital was difficult. There was talk of bringing him to Dublin, Galway, Belfast and even

Glasgow. Luckily, thanks to another baby being transferred elsewhere, a space for a pre-term baby became available in Altnagelvin Area Hospital in Derry. We were advised to have Jack christened, and all I remember was asking the doctor if he was going to die. He couldn't answer me; we said our goodbyes.

The next few weeks were surreal. Our days were filled with meetings with doctors, trying to master medical terminology, checking and monitoring Jack's progress on a day-to-day basis, checking for weight increase and food consumption. The major task for me was expressing milk every two hours. I don't think any parents can get used to seeing their newborn baby hooked up to wires and tubes, to machines flashing and making noises. This was our reality. We felt helpless, alone and exhausted from all the travelling and the crying. There were good days, like the first time we were allowed to hold him, and there were bad days. Unfortunately there were many bad days, namely, when he caught a bug in the NICU and was back in the incubator for another couple of weeks. One step forward and two steps back.

Finally, as the weeks went on, Jack began to get stronger and stronger, first breathing on his own, then feeding, putting on weight, leaving the incubator and being able to regulate his own body temperature. We took him home on a Monday after nearly nine weeks in hospital. We were absolutely delighted and so scared at the same time. We had become so accustomed to Jack being cared for round the clock in the hospital; it had become our way of life, but now he was under our care.

We were walking out of the NICU with a baby, our baby, in the car seat, ready to start life at home as a family. No nurses, no machines and no alarms, just two parents with their first child. The first night was hectic and very warm; we kind of overdid the heat a bit. Like every new parent we kept checking and rechecking that he was sleeping, breathing and warm enough. He had suffered from apnoea (where he would stop breathing) in the hospital, and it was difficult to block the past apnoea episodes from our minds.

Today Jack is three and a half. He has come a long way. He still hasn't been discharged from the hospital as he has had some physical delays. He is seen by many different specialists: paediatricians, physiotherapists, ear, nose and throat specialists, speech and language therapists, occupational therapists, orthopaedic and eye specialists. But he is a very happy, content and loved boy. I hope that our story and stories like ours can help other parents of premature babies see that there is light at the end of the tunnel. It is thanks to Irish Premature Babies that parents of premature babies finally have access to information and support.

Photographs of Jack Falbo.

Jack, just born

Jack, 14 months old

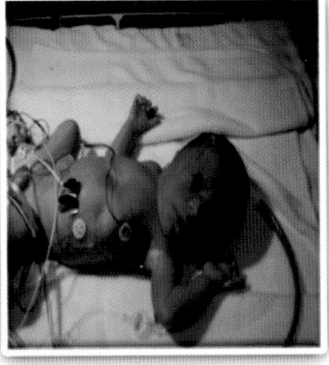

Jack with Maman and Papa

Jack on holidays

CR

James Glacken and Isabelle Glacken
(32 weeks)

In July we discovered that we were expecting twins. Our eldest was 16 months old at the time so it looked like we were going to have a busy house. The pregnancy went very well, and there were no major issues. On 6 December I felt unwell from early morning but by that evening the discomfort had not passed. I rang Mayo General Hospital and was told to come in. At this stage I was 32 weeks pregnant, so having the babies was not really on my mind. I had been given steroid injections earlier in the week to strengthen their lungs as my cervix had dilated slightly, so I should have known that maybe something was about to happen.

When we got to the hospital and I was examined, we discovered that I was fully dilated, so my 'discomfort' at home turned out to be labour pains. A little over an hour later James was born, weighing in at 1.59 kg (3 lb 8 oz), and his sister Isabelle followed 10 minutes later, weighing in at 1.47 kg (3 lb 4 oz). The twins were brought straight to the SCBU where they required some oxygen but luckily did not need any major intervention at that stage. We got to see them some hours later, but I think we were both in shock that these little people had arrived with so little fuss. It was not until the next morning when we went to see them in SCBU that we fully realised the consequence of their early arrival and the lengthy stay they had ahead of them.

I was discharged from hospital three days later and found it so difficult to leave the twins behind. I hoped that after the first time it would get easier. Their stay in hospital progressed nicely, and they put on weight and moved from tube-feeding to bottle-feeding. We got to bathe, feed and change them, and although we could not bring them home it felt good to be involved in their care. When we watched other babies going home we knew that their day would eventually come. One day, Isabelle decided to pull out her feeding tube, so a decision was taken to leave it out and to see how she managed with the bottle-feeding. She loved it and never looked back once the tube came out. At this stage, James had started to bring up his feeds so he was still mainly tube-fed. Eventually he was diagnosed with pyloric stenosis (a condition that causes severe vomiting) and was transferred to Temple Street Children's University Hospital in Dublin where an operation was carried out. After six weeks in hospital, Isabelle came home, and two weeks later her big brother followed.

The delight we had at having them home was short-lived as they were both readmitted to hospital with bronchiolitis, and both had partly collapsed lungs. James became the sicker of the two. As he was still only about 2.04 kg (4 lb 8 oz) and had had a recent operation, he was fairly weak and ended up being resuscitated on the ward. Thankfully the doctors and nurses in Mayo General Hospital were really quick to react to him, and he received immediate attention. That night he was put on a ventilator, and we were told they had done everything they could for him. All we could do was wait and see if he was able to pull through. It was so horrendous, and we couldn't even bear to think about losing our brave little man. We just waited and prayed for a change. The next day he was transferred to Temple Street where he remained on a ventilator for a week before being released home to very happy parents. Isabelle had come home some days earlier and was also fully recovered.

To have them both finally at home with us was such a great joy. We were so careful about hand-washing and visitors to the house as we did not want to risk any reoccurrence of their illness. Hannah, their big sister, who at that point was nearly two, was very protective of 'her babies' and would produce the hand wash to anyone who entered the house. From this stage onwards the twins have been in good health and have only had a couple of hospital stays since, but nothing serious. They were also recently discharged from the care of their consultant so we feel that this is another step forward. Now, at 19 months old, the twins are very healthy and happy little people. They are running around the place and making attempts at speaking. When we look at our babies and remember the tiny little people that came into the world, we can't believe how lucky we are.

Photographs of James Glacken and Isabelle Glacken.

James and Isabelle, six days old, first proper cuddle

James and Isabelle, aged seven months

James and Isabelle, three months with big sister Hannah

James and Isabelle, 19 months with big sister Hannah

CR

James King (27 weeks)

James King was born at 27 weeks by Caesarean section in Mid-Western Regional Maternity Hospital, at 12.45 a.m., weighing 1.08 kg (2 lb 6 oz). My previous two pregnancies and births were fairly normal, but on this pregnancy I had placenta previa and had to be admitted twice to hospital. With James's early arrival, our lives changed completely. I had no idea what went on in the neonatal ward prior to this. My introduction was dramatic and sudden, and now my life revolved totally around the NICU. The outside world passed me by. My new world consisted of beeping monitors, test results and understanding types of medication and feeding issues, and then there were more tests and more results along with constant worry. Worry is a constant companion when your child is in the NICU. You are faced with issues on a daily basis. Each day there is something different to worry about. In the first eight weeks there were ups and downs daily. Sometimes things looked very bad, then things seemed to get better, but the next day something else cropped up and you worried some more. I visited James once every day, sometimes more if I could manage it. My husband John visited in the evenings. For four days I was sick and didn't get to see him. On those days I cried because I didn't get to see him and felt guilty for being sick.

Each day had the same routine. Once I entered the neonatal unit, there was a walk down a long corridor to the ICU. As I got closer to the ward, the beeping from the various monitors got louder, different sounds coming from various machines attached to each baby. Although they alert the nurses to potential problems, those machines don't half make parents anxious. Anxiety and worry would start to rise within me as I approached the intensive-care door. Straight away I would look to James's incubator and check his monitors. I would breathe a sigh of relief when his monitors weren't making any noise. The relief was usually only temporary. When you have a child in NICU, worry is always there in the background. It never completely leaves you.

They say it's good for babies to hear your voice so James and I would have a little chat. I used to tell him what his sisters and daddy were up to that day. I tried to remain upbeat as I held his tiny hand with my fingers. It's so difficult, especially in the beginning, to come to terms with what is happening, to understand the many medical issues that face a premature baby on their daily battle to stay alive. I would try to remain positive when I was with James. My daily mantras for him were, 'You can do it!' and 'You can come through this.'

The fifth week was the toughest time for us. On the Monday I had visited James as usual that morning and he had seemed to be struggling. By late afternoon he was getting worse. John and I went in to see him again that night, and on the way to the hospital the consultant phoned to say that James was on the ventilator again. He was deemed to have a serious infection. When we saw him, my heart sank as I thought that he wouldn't make it through the night. I still remember how he looked as he lay in the incubator: grey. I watched the ventilator doing all the breathing for him. I feared the worst. I tried to remain positive but could feel the tears start as I looked at him. Later I lay in bed wondering if I had got it wrong. Maybe he wouldn't come through this.

The next 24 hours were awful. Tests were done to ascertain exactly what type of infection he had. More X-rays were done along with a lumbar puncture. He was going through more medical procedures then I had ever had done in my life. He had more antibiotics in the first two months than I ever had in my life, and he was so tiny.

Eventually he came through it all, and by early December he had 'turned a corner'. In January 2010, just before his due date, my little man came home. My introduction to the NICU was traumatic, but I now felt very sad to be leaving. It's difficult to explain. I was delighted that James could leave, but it was daunting at the same time. It's hard to let go of the safety net of hospital care and to go it alone. I wondered if I would manage and if James would be alright without the machines monitoring him.

James is now a happy healthy todder, and NICU seems like a lifetime ago. Thank God he is doing well, very happy and also a very determined little man.

Photographs of James King.

James, three days old

James, three weeks old

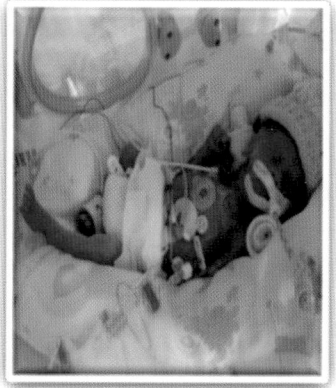

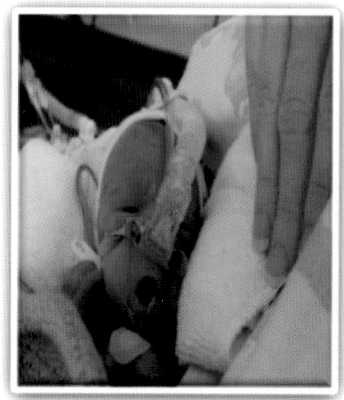

James, aged 18 months

James, having lots of fun

⍑

Jason Behan (24 weeks)

Our story began in the Coombe Women and Infants University Hospital in Dublin. On 29 January, our son Jason arrived weighing 0.57 kg (1 lb 4 oz), 16 weeks early. I can't remember much about his first week of life, as I was recovering from pre-eclampsia. I can recall travelling from my room to the NICU three or four times a day to deliver my EBM. I remember getting a quick look at my small soldier in his incubator each time I delivered the milk. He resembled a little pink frog with his head no bigger than a small mandarin orange.

I went home a week later. My battle was over, but his was only beginning. I was only home a day when we received a phone call to say that Jason had an infection. This was to be the start of the roller-coaster ride that comes with having a baby in an NICU. The first 12 weeks of Jason's life were the hardest we have ever known. He required high-frequency ventilation due to his immature and undeveloped lungs. Although he only had a few infections during this time, he required two courses of steroids, as well as a lumbar puncture, when bacterial meningitis was suspected. He had infective endocarditis (an infection in the heart) and a pulmonary embolism (blood clot on the lung). He had anaemia and required many blood transfusions. At times, he was so heavily sedated and swollen it was hard to sit and look at him. At times, he was very agitated, and some days we couldn't even touch him. After 10 weeks of staring at him through the glass of his incubator, I finally got to hold him.

In April Jason travelled to Our Lady's Children's Hospital in Crumlin for laser treatment on both eyes due to an eye condition called ROP. A week later he was moved off the full ventilation onto CPAP. On his actual due date, 17 May, Jason came off CPAP and went onto oxygen via nasal prongs, a very proud moment and a delight to be able to finally see his handsome face. Over the next month he had a few minor setbacks, putting him on and off CPAP before finally settling to nasal prongs.

On 27 June Jason was transferred down to the SCBU in Portlaoise Hospital, my local hospital, as he was doing well. No longer did I have to make the hour-and-a-half-long trek up to Dublin. I could now come and go as I pleased as we only lived 15 minutes away. Unfortunately the change of hospital didn't suit Jason, and he ended up back on antibiotics and in an oxygen headbox with up to 15 litres of oxygen at times to keep his vital statistics stable. He also went off all oral feeds and back onto a feeding tube into his stomach. We had taken one step forward and about 10 steps back.

It took two weeks before Jason settled back to himself, although he was still reluctant to suck a bottle. At the end of July, Jason was 'promoted' to the paediatric ward. He was growing a bit big (and bold) for the already crowded SCBU, and I was finding it difficult to offer him the stimulation he needed. I couldn't believe the freedom with the move. We had our own room, we could tell stories, sing out of tune, have sleepovers and, best of all, finally share him with our friends and family. During this time Jason required two long stays in Temple Street Children's University Hospital in Dublin. On one occasion he had pulmonary oedema (fluid in the lungs) and the other time was for a bowel obstruction and hernia operation. Incidentally, it was there, on 1 September, that he gave me his first smile.

Following this, plans were set for his discharge. As Jason was unable to suck a bottle we were supplied with an infinity pump in order to tube-feed him. We also had to arrange for home oxygen, monitors, syringes and other day-to-day medical supplies. We had several day trips home with Jason before the final discharge to avoid any obstacles that might arise with his new equipment. On 29 September Jason came home exactly eight months after he was born and we finally became a family.

Nothing and nobody can prepare you for having a baby in an NICU: the stress of being there and the guilt of not, sharing the ups and downs with others and the incredible bond that you make with the staff. Every parent of a premature child will recall the adrenalin rush of changing a nappy in an incubator, seeing their baby open their little black eyes and finally feeling their little miracle in their arms.

Photographs of Jason Behan.

Jason, two days old

Jason, 73 days old

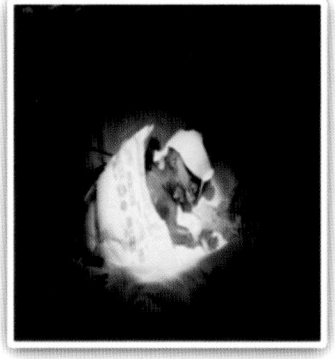
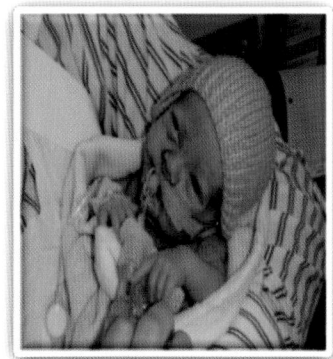

Jason, seven months old

Jason, 18 months old

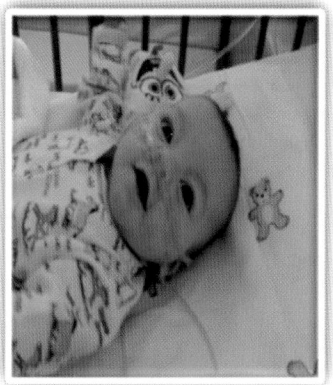

Jay Byrne and Rocco Byrne (32 weeks)

In April 2007, I was 32 weeks pregnant, and my husband Nicky and I had just come home from a few weeks travelling on the road with the Irish band Westlife. It had not been the most comfortable of times, being pregnant with twins on a tour bus, attending concerts, etc. I was happy and relieved when we got back home to Dublin, thinking we had at least a couple of weeks to get ready. At last I was able to put my feet up and prepare for the exciting arrival of our precious baby boys.

Soon after we settled in back home we went to visit Nicky's parents; I remember it was a Wednesday. While we were there, they presented us with two adorable carrycots. We were so excited, and later that night, when we got home, we placed the carrycots in the twins' room with the scan photos in each one, imagining how things would be on their arrival.

Looking back on that day, I can clearly remember going to bed that night, thinking perhaps something was about to begin a wee bit too early. That next morning, we dashed into the NMH in Dublin, where I discovered I was going into premature labour. In the early hours of Friday, 20 April, the boys were delivered by emergency Caesarean section, eight weeks prematurely. And so began our journey into the world of precious premature babies.

While we were so very grateful and ecstatic that we had two healthy and perfectly well babies, we were at the same time filled with worry and concern as they were so small. Later on that night, a little weary and upset after the delivery, we were brought up to the NICU to meet our little boys. They were just so beautiful and perfect, but ever so tiny. One of the boys weighed 1.28 kg (2 lb 13 oz) and the other one weighed

1.64 kg (3 lb 10 oz). We were very lucky to be able to have kangaroo care with our babies that night and really treasure those first early moments with the boys.

It was heartbreaking when it was time to put our babies back into their incubators and leave them for the night. For seven months of my pregnancy they had been with me all the time, and I found the separation very hard. I could hear other mothers together with their babies through the corridors of the hospital. However, I quickly established a routine and looked forward to every visit and feed with my boys. There were times when it was very difficult, for instance when we heard our babies crying or looking distressed or when they pulled out their feeding tubes. This was very worrying, as we just desperately wanted them to get enough of a feed in order to gain sufficient weight so they could come home.

The nurses kept in close contact with us to ensure that we were present for feeds, nappy changes, cuddles and baths, and I still felt close to the babies while I was in the hospital. However, when my stay in hospital was up and it was time to be discharged, we were devastated. It was a very emotional time, and this was exacerbated by my pregnancy hormones going crazy. Being separated from our babies was so difficult. I felt guilty every time I thought of them all alone in hospital in their incubators. Throughout the pregnancy they were in the womb, cosy together, and now I could not even cuddle or hold them.

Looking back, it's difficult to explain when it seems such a short space of time to be parted, but for parents of newborn infants it's hard to contemplate leaving your newborn babies to one side never mind leaving them in hospital. We headed home, not knowing how long it would be before they would be home with us. I tried to focus on the positive feedback from the hospital staff who were constantly reassuring us of how well and healthy our two little men were and that they were thriving each step of the way. The amazing teams in the

NICUs around the country work tirelessly for so many premature babies, some of whom are far more unwell than our boys. They are amazing, and we will be forever grateful that our two boys received this amazing start in life.

The pain of being unable to hold the boys from the moment they were born, that instant separation, was incredibly difficult and left me feeling so lonely without them. I got to take one baby home whilst having to leave his twin in hospital, an occasion tinged with both sadness and guilt. All I wanted to do was stay at home and snuggle and feed them together. Taking premature babies home from hospital is not without its complications. Understandably, as a new parent I was dying to show off my new arrivals, but that sometimes had to take a back seat in favour of the constant follow-up appointments for eyes, ears, heart, etc., as well as many more developmental check-ups down the line. Those first weeks are fraught with worry and are just so very busy. Every car journey is a nerve-wracking one for a new parent as premature babies are almost too small to fit into their huge car seats. After three very long and emotional weeks we finally got to take both our boys home. Four years later we are blessed to have two wonderful healthy boys.

My reasons for coming on board and supporting the Irish Premature Babies is because whether you're a first-time mother or not, having a premature baby is a daunting experience. Support groups and parents who understand your journey are a wonderful resource for parents who presently have babies in the NICU. For my hubby and I, it was a very short moment in time, and from the moment we took our gorgeous, healthy, tiny babies home there was no looking back. Thankfully, since then they both have been well and perfectly healthy, but for many other parents there can be many other health implications to contend with and developmental problems to overcome. I fully empathise with the parents of premature babies who experience the heartbreak of leaving their little ones in the hospital and the overwhelming worry of not knowing if they are going to be OK and grow and be like every other baby.

Photographs of Jay Byrne and Rocco Byrne.

Rocco and Jay looking very cute

Jay and Rocco with Daddy and Mammy

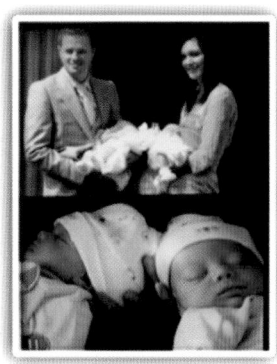

Family picture

The boys with Mammy and Daddy

Jessica Cooling (24 weeks)

On 20 April I gave birth to a very beautiful, very precious but also very tiny baby girl called Jessica. She was born at 24 weeks' gestation and weighed 0.7 kg (1 lb 9 oz). After we had a brief glimpse of her tiny body in the incubator, Jessica was taken away from us and transferred straight to NICU. Three hours later we arrived in the NICU. We were shown to Jessica's incubator, and we were in shock, not only because of her size and transparent skin but because she had so many wires and lines attached to her. She was hooked up to lots of machines. We were completely overwhelmed. It took many weeks to become accustomed to the NICU. We learnt what every monitor was for, what the different noises were, when Jessica's feeding time was. We memorised her routine. Eventually we were allowed to help with her care, and that helped us feel closer to her. The doctor explained to us that even though Jessica was stable we faced a roller-coaster ahead. He advised us not to get our hopes up. So, day by day, we learnt how to care for our daughter, and each evening our hearts would break leaving her behind. We called the unit nightly to check on her progress. They would tell us she gained 10 grams, maybe 30 grams, but one night they informed us that she had gained 90 grams, and our hopes shot up. She was getting closer to 0.91 kg (2 lb). In hindsight, this was so out of the ordinary, but that was our life and 'the norm' as far as we were concerned.

After a month in the NICU, Jessica was improving enough to move to the HDU, and on the same day her weight went up to 0.91 kg (2 lb). We were ecstatic, and our hopes were high, but at the same time we were realistic. We knew there was still a long way to go and that things could turn very quickly.

Jessica's stomach bloated out quite a lot, and they told us this could be NEC, which was highly dangerous to her health. She would be taken off feeds, given blood transfusions if required and monitored closely. Luckily though it resolved and thankfully never led to anything too complicated. It did set her back on her journey quite a bit as it stalled her progress with feeding. We were just happy that she was still with us.

One of the scariest moments was when I was holding her on my chest and I had her all snuggled up and cosy. I was sitting back in the chair and could hear the monitor beeping but could not see it. I wasn't too concerned because when she was out the monitor would usually go off due to her movement from Jessica and the wires that were attached to her. There was a doctor sitting on the other side of the incubator. He stood up to check the monitor and immediately called the nurse to take Jessica off me. When they took the blanket off, her body was completely grey and translucent. They asked me to wait outside, and I broke down in tears. Some of the other mothers came out to reassure me. Eventually, after what seemed like an hour but what was only about 10 minutes, the nurse came out to tell me that she was fine and explained that this happens quite a lot with premature babies. The nurse then showed me what to do if this happened again. Bradycardias and apnoeas became more normal. Jessica would stop breathing and would need a gentle reminder to start breathing again. From then on, whenever it happened, I would just tap her bum a few times, and she would remember to breathe again. It was a very scary experience, but, funnily, I got used to it. After a couple of weeks it didn't scare me as much. It became part of the routine.

Jessica finally got moved to SCBU, and after three months of waiting and anticipation we were allowed to take her home. We felt like the proudest parents in Ireland. There were a lot of appointments following her hospital stay, but I am happy to say Jessica is now a happy, healthy three-year-old, and you would never guess that she had the journey that she had. We will forever be proud of our little miracle. Her determination to never give up gave us hope and strength and instilled in us the courage to never give up.

Photographs of Jessica Cooling.

Jessica, nine days old

Jessica, four weeks old

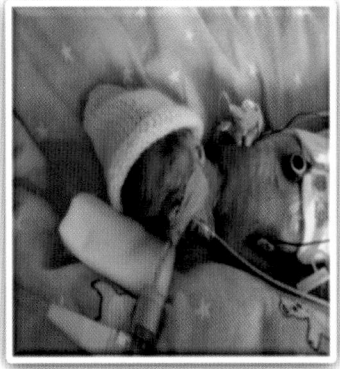

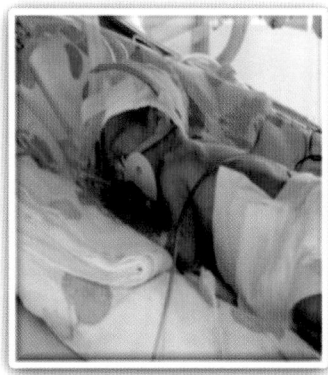

Jessica, eight weeks old

Jessica, 10 weeks old

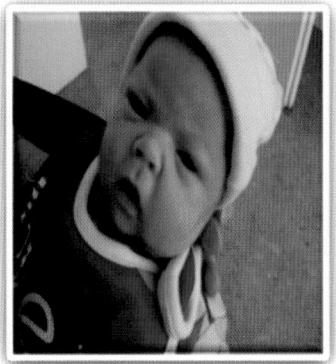

ଔ

Joe Harrison (30 weeks)

My first pregnancy had been pretty uneventful until 27 weeks when I got a ferocious pain and decided to go straight to hospital thinking I had pulled a muscle. My blood pressure was through the roof, with no sign of it steadying or coming down, and I was kept in hospital. I was given steroid injections to help develop the baby's lungs and was monitored closely. I was scanned every second day and put on different medications, but I still felt completely terrified. The novelty of scans soon wore off, but the one good thing was that we found out our baby's sex. Initially I didn't want to, but I think I needed to know to whom I was talking while in hospital.

It really is the last thing you expect on your first pregnancy. I was 30 years of age, with absolutely no history of any pregnancy complications in either of our families. Those weeks in hospital before Joe was born I tried to prepare myself for every eventuality, including the worst. Then, on 21 December, as I called into ultrasound as normal for a scan, at 30 weeks, things started to change. During the scan I knew by the look on everyone's faces that something was up. It was only when I was told 'baby's coming out' that the realisation of being mother to a premature baby hit me.

I had prepared by telling myself that I wouldn't hear the baby because the doctors might have to work on him before he breathed on his own and considered the possibility that he might have complications with his health and so on. However, not only did he kick my doctor when she delivered him by emergency section, but he also screamed the theatre down as soon as he was born, at 2.35 p.m., all 1.45 kg (3 lb 3 oz) of him.

Joe was taken to the NICU by the paediatricians after a brief hello to my husband and me. I was brought to recovery and eventually back to my room where my mam was waiting for me. My blood pressure continued to be haywire for the rest of the day, so it was nearly 10.30 p.m. before I was brought up to the NICU for a proper look at my son – probably the eight longest hours of my life. I went up to see him, and he was in the main area of the unit on a CPAP machine, no ventilator required. He was also under a bili light. I was allowed up to see him for 10 minutes, which seemed to fly by in seconds. Reluctantly my husband brought me back down to my room where I did not sleep a wink all night, mainly due to the fact that I was ecstatic but still terrified.

The following morning I went up to see my boy in the NICU. He was barely a day old and yet I recognised his cry. He had been moved to a room off the side of main NICU, and he had also been taken off CPAP and was breathing on his own – still under a bili light, but thriving. He was being tube-fed, but only TPN as his digestive system was slightly compromised because of the problems with the blood flow to my placenta. This rectified itself in a few days, and his first feed of EBM was a giant 3 ml.

Joe went from strength to strength, spending only a week in the NICU before being moved to the SCBU. There he thrived even more steadily, gaining weight and growing. Joe came home on 27 January, after rooming in with me the night before. I was delighted to have him all to myself. Needless to say I didn't sleep a wink that night, I just kept staring at him. He was five weeks and two days old, and nobody only his mam and dad had seen him because of swine-flu restrictions. How excited and relieved we were to be bringing him home. He now weighed 2.38 kg (5 lb 4 oz).

From being fed 3 ml at that first feed, Joe has turned into a food demolisher, head wrecker, sleep depriver, lifestyle curtailer, and we wouldn't change him for the world. Every

Tiny Footprints

snotty kiss, dirty nappy and 'Ah ah, don't eat that Joe, it's dirty' enriches our lives.

Photographs of Joe Harrison.

Joe under bili lights

Joe, doing kangaroo care

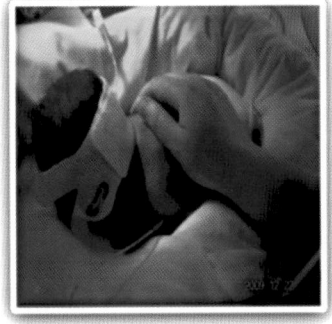

Joe, nine months old

Joe

Josh Rafter Kendellen (34 weeks)

On 3 February, a Wednesday morning, my waters broke. I was admitted to St Luke's General Hospital in Kilkenny where I was told my baby would arrive sooner than expected. At 33 weeks, I was scared but a bit excited also. I went into labour on the Saturday, and Josh was born the following day at 34 weeks, weighing 2.64 kg (5 lb 13 oz). I saw him briefly as the team of paediatric doctors checked him out and whisked him off to SCBU.

I didn't get to see Josh again until the following day as I'd had a Caesarean section. That was very tough having him but not having him beside me. He had no breathing problems as I'd had the steroid injections to develop his lungs when I was pregnant. When I first saw him in SCBU it was such a shock to see him with wires and tubes. I remember thinking how unnatural it is to be whisked out of his comfort zone into an incubator. It was an overwhelming feeling when I first walked in an SCBU, and I think I was in a state of shock. This was not how our lives together should begin.

Thankfully, Josh had only minor setbacks although at the time I didn't realise how lucky I was that they were only minor complications or issues. It's such a roller-coaster of emotions and so far removed from the outside world. Josh was on antibiotics to prevent possible infections. The main setbacks he had were feeding and recurrent jaundice. He spent time on and off the bili bed over the next two weeks. There were concerns about the bones in his skull being overlapped, although I wasn't made aware at that time. Another issue was feeding. Josh needed to be feeding by himself and keeping it down for 48 hours before he could go home. Unfortunately, he got tired easily and ended up finishing his feeds via tube.

He had severe reflux which meant he brought his feed back up even if we didn't move him. Eventually he turned a corner and got a little stronger. He was able to feed a little longer and kept a bit more down. Finally we took him home, where he has turned into a happy, healthy, much-loved and loving little man.

Photographs of Josh Rafter Kendellen.

Josh, a few hours old

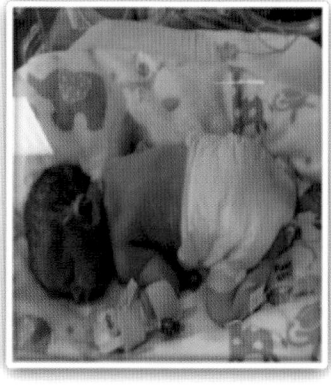

Josh after one week

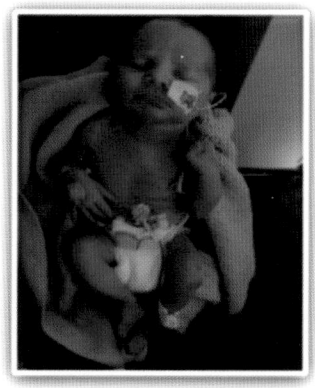

Josh, having a well-deserved nap

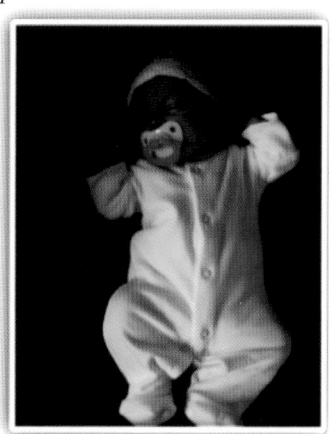

Josh today, at 20 months

Kacey Hulgraine (31 weeks) and Rebecca Hulgraine (34 weeks)

We are the proud parents of two beautiful and cheeky little girls who both arrived early. Our eldest girl, Rebecca, was born on 28 October at 31 weeks, weighing 1.4 kg (3 lb). She screamed shortly after delivery and was brought straight to the NICU where she was placed on CPAP for 72 hours. In the first few days her weight dropped to 1.2 kg (2 lb 10 oz) and she got a kidney infection. We hoped that the antibiotics would work quickly, and luckily they did, with Rebecca slowly gaining weight. It was such a relief to see her weight slowly rising day by day, gram by gram; she was getting closer to home. After a few weeks, she was breathing on her own and we were learning how to cope with such a tiny baby, how to change and how to feed our little girl. Then, to our absolute delight, we passed our first milestone: Rebecca was transferred to a cot and moved out of the NICU to the SCBU. This was such a big deal to us, as in the SCBU Rebecca thrived and quickly gained enough weight to come home. Four weeks after she was born we brought Rebecca home, weighing 2.1 kg (4 lb 6 oz).

On discharge from hospital, we had fortnightly check-ups to monitor her weight and physiotherapy appointments to check for suspected cerebral palsy due to muscle weakness. Thankfully, however, after spending a few months with Enable Ireland and getting a comprehensive exercise programme to carry out at home, Rebecca was discharged by the age of 20 months. Now we have no worries about Rebecca, she is an amazing little girl who thankfully has no lasting effects from her prematurity. She is a bright and happy child who is now almost three. She is well able to have full conversations with family and friends, she can count from 1 to 10 and loves to say the alphabet. She is also a super big sister to Kacey.

Kacey was born on 22 December the following year, at 34 weeks' gestation, weighing 1.6 kg (3 lb 9 oz). She spent 24 hours in the NICU, with just five hours on CPAP. Then she only needed small amounts of oxygen periodically. Kacey was quickly moved to a ward to focus on weight gain, which turned out to be quite problematic. It was very hard for us all as it was Christmas and the weather was awful, with bad snow, so it was difficult to get to the hospital to visit her as much as we wanted to. Kacey didn't feed easily and was very slow to put on weight, but thankfully, after 20 days, she was discharged. Kacey now copies everything her big sister does.

As their mammy, my sole concern was for my babies, but my partner Michael, their dad, had more stress and worry, as I was not well and he was so worried about me as well as the girls. He was also the one left with the job of communicating with all our family and friends who were so concerned. Michael did a fantastic job looking after us all, and I will be forever grateful to him for being so strong and supportive during a very emotional time. He is still the one who holds me when I have a mini-breakdown thinking of how stressful it all was and how much I blamed myself.

I don't know for sure if it was the premature births that contributed to my PND, but I believe it to be quite common. All I know is that it was present in me from when Rebecca was born but I ignored it until I was a few months pregnant with Kacey. If I can share one message to other mums feeling low, it is to tell someone. No one is going to think you don't love or accept your child – this was my big fear until I was truthful to my nurse who encouraged me to talk to my doctor and get the help I needed. I went on medication after Kacey was born and began to feel and see everything much more clearly than before.

After the birth of both Rebecca and Kacey I felt so cheated at not being able to cradle and have my babies in a cot beside me, to be the one who fed them and changed their nappies, but those negative memories fade when you get your little mite home and you become the real parent then. We are so grateful for our amazing girls. We have a beautiful bond, and we wouldn't change them for the world. It is just so important to believe in your baby and in yourself!

Photographs of Kacey Hulgraine and Rebecca Hulgraine.

Kacey, two days old

Kacey, aged 15 months

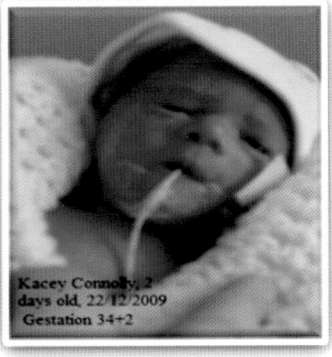

Rebecca's first picture

Rebecca, 37 months

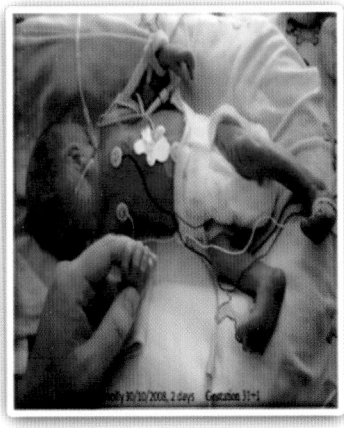

Keely Wendling (27 weeks)

Our beautiful little princess Keely arrived into the world 13 weeks early on 13 February 2007. She was born prematurely due to complications of PPROM which I had suffered from 18 weeks in my pregnancy. Keely weighed in at a tiny 0.96 kg (2 lb 2 oz) and had a very severe battle in front of her. Keely was whisked away to the NICU within minutes, and it was a few hours before I got to see her again. Not being able to hold her and seeing her being pulled and prodded right before my very eyes was destroying although I knew it was for her benefit. My first glimpse of my little girl was a bittersweet moment. While I instantly fell in love with this tiny little person, it just felt so wrong that she should be going through so many traumas.

Within hours of her birth it was decided that Keely would require high-frequency ventilation which was not available in her birth hospital in Drogheda so she was transferred by the neonatal transfer team to the NMH in Dublin. Considering the bleak outlook that Keely had been given we decided to have our little girl christened immediately before her transfer. On reflection it was more like last rites than a christening, but it did offer us some comfort.

Keely spent a very tough two weeks in Holles Street where she had a grade-2 bleed to her brain, a PDA and also contracted MRSA. When Keely was five days old, I got to have my first cuddle with her. I reluctantly gave her back to the nurses after a few minutes, and, if I am honest, all I wanted to do was to run out of there with my little sweetheart and take her home with me.

Life became a roller-coaster of emotions from the second Keely arrived into this world. Having an 18-month-old baby at home also made the process very difficult. I really felt torn between being at home and being up at the hospital. There were so many days when I felt that if I could just split myself into two I would. It was very hard to have hope but we were inspired every day by the fight that our little princess had inside.

Once Keely stabilised a little she was moved back to Drogheda. Once again, she took several turns, and it became a regular occurrence to walk into the unit holding our breath in fear of what new problem we would face that day. Our little girl battled day in and day out with MRSA but she never gave up.

Her weight became a huge issue as she was not gaining at the rate she should have been. It soon became apparent that our tiny girl was lactose intolerant. I found the whole process very difficult at the time as expressing breastmilk had been the one thing I felt I could do for my baby, and now suddenly I couldn't even do that. In hindsight now I realise that there was nothing I could have done.

Keely was then diagnosed with ROP, so once again we found ourselves in the position of having to transfer back to Holles Street for surgery. Once Keely got to 10 weeks she seemed to suddenly make huge strides in her recovery. She was moved out of an incubator and into a cot. She went from being tube-fed one day to being able to tolerate feeds from a bottle. Eventually the magical day that always seemed so out of reach suddenly came and I got the phone call that I had longed for so much. Our princess was coming home.

Having Keely home was the most magical moment. We finally got to introduce her to her big brother and all her loving family who for many weeks had longed to meet her. The excitement was huge, as you can imagine. Keely came on in leaps and bounds. While not making her milestones exactly on time, with the help of the early-intervention team in the Central Remedial Clinic in Dublin and her doctors and nurses, she has come on excellently. Keely is now a very happy and fun-loving little four-year-old girl who lives life to the full. She has excelled in so many ways, and she continually amazes us and brings such joy into our lives.

Photographs of Keely Wendling.

Keely, one day old, on
ventilation

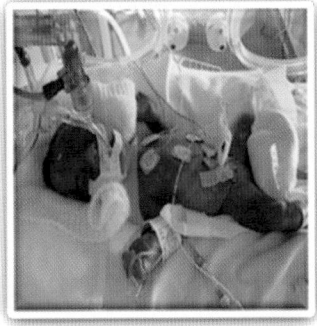

First cuddle with Daddy,
eight days old

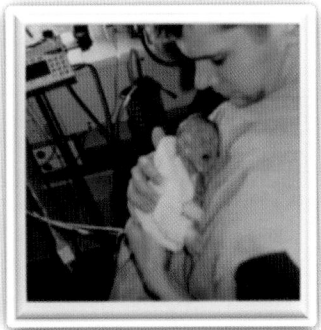

Cuddle time with Mummy in
the NICU

Keely aged four getting
ready for primary school

Kelly Anne Kathleen O'Neill (31 weeks)

At my 20-week scan on my first pregnancy, a routine blood-pressure check revealed that my blood pressure was slightly elevated, so my doctor decided to keep an eye on things. Two weeks later it was still high, so I was put on a blood-pressure monitor for 24 hours and given a letter for my next hospital visit. Six weeks later, at my next check-up, I felt fine but was sent straight to St Luke's General Hospital in Kilkenny. There a scan showed the growth of the baby was small for dates and so I was sent to Waterford Regional Hospital as they had an SCBU. Although my baby was 28 weeks' gestation at this stage, it was only the size of a 21-week-old fetus, and my blood pressure was still sky-high.

The medical team at Waterford carried out lots of tests to ascertain what was going on. I had numerous scans, blood tests and blood-pressure checks, and eventually they diagnosed pre-eclampsia. Usually with this condition your ankles and hands get very swollen, but mine were not, which had made it more difficult to pin down. My baby was growing, but very slowly and would have to be born early, but they couldn't determine when. The longer the baby was growing and moving the safer it was for both baby and me, and so we just had to wait and see. At 31 weeks, I was sent to the NMH in Dublin for additional tests to assess the health of the baby and to determine the cause of the slow growth. On Wednesday, 24 November, an ambulance brought me to Dublin for the tests, and we were told the results would be back in a week. However, when I got back to Waterford, I had another scan, and the doctors decided it was time to deliver my baby. I was 31 weeks and 5 days at this point.

A nurse from the SCBU explained to my husband and I what would happen when the baby was born, and everybody seemed so calm and relaxed that we felt very reassured. Our beautiful baby girl, Kelly Anne Kathleen O'Neill was born, weighing in at 0.85 kg (1 lb 14 oz). I only saw her for a few seconds before she was taken away in an incubator. Later, my husband went to see her in the SCBU.

He showed me pictures of our daughter and told me that she had held his finger. She looked so small I couldn't believe it. When I was wheeled up to see my baby for myself I was amazed to see that she was breathing on her own, a real fighter from day 1. Kelly Anne stayed in the SCBU for two days, and during that time I didn't get to hold her. She was so small that her body was unable to regulate her temperature.

The nurses explained to me that breastfeeding would be the best for Kelly Anne, and although I had decided that I wasn't going to breastfeed, I quickly changed my mind. Kelly Anne came first, and I needed to do whatever I could to help, so I began to express breastmilk. She initially started on just 1 ml of EBM. It was a very slow process, but each day she took a little more. I was let home after five days, which I found very difficult. It was so hard to leave Kelly Anne in the hospital. But the doctors reassured us that she was doing well and that we just had to take it day by day.

Kelly Anne started to put on weight and to drink more, and some days we even got to dress her in clothes, which was lovely as she looked much bigger when dressed. She reached 1.3 kg (2 lb 14 oz), but it was around this time that she contracted MRSA. Thankfully, as she was getting bigger and stronger, it didn't affect her too badly, and by mid-January she was clear of the infection. She continued to put on weight slowly, taking increasing volumes of EBM at each feed, but she was moving so much in the incubator that she was nearly burning the weight gain off as fast.

Finally, after spending 72 days travelling up and down to Waterford, we got to bring her home. It was 14 February, and the best Valentine's present anybody could wish for. Since Kelly Anne's discharge from hospital we have had many appointments and check-ups, and thankfully she is going great. She is a very happy little girl, constantly talking and full of energy. She is still absolutely tiny, and her weight is slow to catch up, but that might be due to the fact that she never stops running around.

Photographs of Kelly Anne Kathleen O'Neill.

Kelly Anne, one day old

Four days old, Daddy's first hold

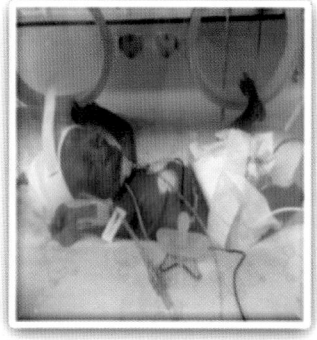

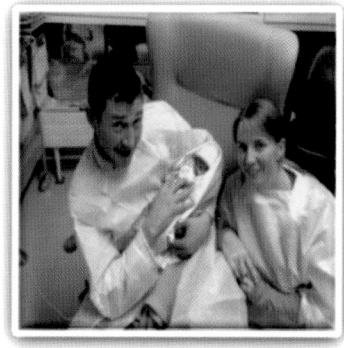

Kelly Anne, six months old

Kelly Anne's first birthday

CR

Leo Shorten (34 weeks)

Leo is an only child, and his conception was a huge surprise to myself and Joan after 14 years of marriage, so we started out on the pregnancy with a feeling that luck was on our side. However, once he stopped growing in Joan's womb, it became apparent that we would be seeing him sooner rather than later. At that time we began to feel unlucky, especially when our consultant hinted with increasing frequency that Leo might have Down Syndrome. Although we were both depressed by this and worried for the baby's future, we continued to hope for the best and to convince ourselves that he might be fine.

When we saw him on the scan monitor, we knew he was a boy, and his facial features were the exact same when he was born. Although I felt that I already knew him, I was still unprepared for his early arrival. While we had hoped he would stay inside for much longer, and grow, we had been warned that a Caesarean section was definite unless his progress improved. It hadn't been decided when the Caesarean would be, but Joan received steroids to help develop the baby's lungs only a few days prior to his birth.

Given Leo's low weight and lack of growth, our consultant in the Rotunda Hospital in Dublin was monitoring Joan with increasing frequency, and, as it turned out, a visit had been scheduled for the morning of Leo's birth. Following a small bleeding incident at 7.30 a.m., we rang the hospital and brought the time forward. Joan was immediately monitored for about half an hour before our consultant arrived. He was concerned enough for our baby's welfare that he decided on a Caesarean section immediately. Joan was in shock and physically shaking at the speed of everything, and I was left behind in the commotion. I was told a few minutes later to make my way to the operating theatre. I took a seat in the inside area where various male staff smiled encouragingly at me, and one gave me the thumbs-up. I was soon shown the changing room where I put on surgical scrubs and overshoes and went through the swing door to join Joan in the theatre. I sat on a stool right up beside Joan's head (she told me afterwards that she did initially wonder who was this strange, silent doctor staring at her wide-eyed over his mask) and did my best to reassure her while staying out of the way. I was excited, anxious and emotional all at the same time.

As Leo was small, the surgeon matched his size to the incision, so there was as little cutting as possible, and the operation moved very swiftly. At 10.21 a.m., at 34 weeks' gestation, we saw Leo for the first time, all 1.39 kg (3 lb 1 oz) of him, and this will always be one of the most memorable experiences of my life. He was held up by the legs for about three seconds by our consultant who announced, 'Joan, here is your baby', before being passed for assessment to a nurse. The scene made a big impression on me, and for the following two years I would replay it often, holding Leo up and announcing, 'Here is your baby!' to Joan – something she quickly tired of.

Leo was taken away to be checked by nursing staff and for his umbilical-cord oxygen levels to be assessed as an indication of the distress that he may have gone through prior to birth. Within the hour, our consultant called to the room with the very good news that Leo would not need to be tested for Down Syndrome. Although small, he would be fine following a stay in hospital. We were overjoyed.

During the following five weeks, Joan put in long days at the hospital while I did weekday evenings and weekends with her. They were stressful and very emotional times, but we were buoyed up by the wonderful photographs of other premature babies on the walls of the parents' room and by their subsequent development. Kangaroo care was a very special experience, holding Leo for short periods inside my shirt with all the tubes attached. When my father-in-law and sister-in-law were allowed in for a visit they marvelled at his small size but were too afraid to hold him.

Leo was discharged at about 1.96 kg (4 lb 5 oz), five weeks after his birth, on New Year's Eve. I am very conscious how lucky we are that it all went well for our little boy, who is now such a happy, active child without any ongoing health issues.

Photographs of Leo Shorten.

Leo, looking like butter wouldn't melt

Leo with his rabbit Lapin and their matching convict outfits

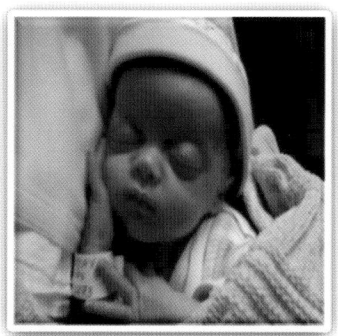

Enjoying kangaroo care with Dad for the first time

Our special guy has come a long way, happy, healthy and almost five

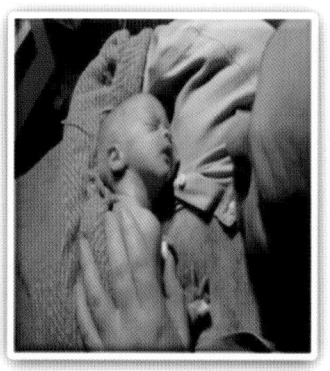

CR

Leon Woods (27 weeks)

My pregnancy with Leon started off as normal until a bleed at 25 weeks. I went straight to the Rotunda Hospital in Dublin, where I spent three days and was given steroids to help mature the baby's lungs in case of an early delivery. Then, at 27 weeks, I began to haemorrhage very badly at home and was rushed to hospital by ambulance.

At the hospital, the staff struggled to find the baby's heartbeat and discovered that part of my membranes had ruptured. A further scan confirmed that my baby was still alive but that my waters hadn't broken. The plan was to try to keep the baby inside me for as long as possible, and so I was admitted until delivery. I had myself prepared for a long time lying in the hospital waiting, but this was not the case as the very next day I started getting cramps which became increasingly worse as the day progressed.

By 11.00 p.m. that night, I was 2 cm dilated, and I was moved to the labour ward. It was a slow labour, and I was getting very tired, so when I eventually got to 5 cm they decided to break my waters, and at 7.00 a.m. on 11 March, Leon was born weighing 1.19 kg (2 lb 10 oz). I didn't get to see my son immediately after he was born. My husband and I were very emotional as he was rushed away to the NICU. There were problems with the delivery of my placenta, and so I was taken to theatre for operation where I lost a lot of blood. I was very weak afterwards, and so it was 8.00 p.m. that night before I got to see my son. Leon didn't look like a newborn baby. He was so tiny, his head, face and feet were black, his skin had cuts, and he was covered in wires and tubes, with tape on his elbows and knees to protect his skin.

After a week of waiting, I eventually got to have the moment I had missed out on after Leon was born: I finally got to hold my son. It felt so great to have his skin against mine, although it was scary too. He was so tiny and thin, and I was afraid I was going to hurt him. Leon had RDS and was ventilated for one day, and then he moved to CPAP for four weeks and eventually onto oxygen prongs for a further eight weeks. During his time in the NICU, he had a grade-2 bleed in the brain, a heart condition called PDA, CLD and five blood transfusions.

Leon was fully tube-fed for six weeks, and when I gave him his first bottle he had trouble feeding as he found it hard to suck, breathe and swallow. Sometimes he would forget to breathe altogether, and the alarms would go off and frighten the life out of us. The fact that he had reflux also didn't help, and often it would take a full hour to feed him only for him to bring it all back up again. His feeding issues were very difficult to cope with, and we struggled through those first few weeks, but every day it got a little bit easier. Eventually, at eight weeks, his feeding tube was removed as he was doing much better with his feeds, and it was so nice to see his face properly – albeit red from the tape that had been holding his tubes in place.

After nine weeks and two days, we were told that he was almost ready for discharge, and on 16 May we took our little boy home. We were filled with a mixture of both dread and excitement. We were very anxious, not knowing what to expect. Unfortunately, Leon was unable to tolerate his feeds very well at home so we ended up back in the hospital the following day. There it was discovered his red blood cells were low so he was given another blood transfusion, and finally, four days later, Leon came home for good.

Leon is now three years old. He is the smartest and funniest little boy, who lights up all our lives. He suffers with recurrent chest infections, and he is on two inhalers a day. He also has some sensory issues and has lower gross motor skills than other children his age, but this is improving. Apart from the scars on his hands, you would never know the hardship our little miracle boy has been through.

Photographs of Leon Woods.

Leon, one day old

Leon, 12 days old

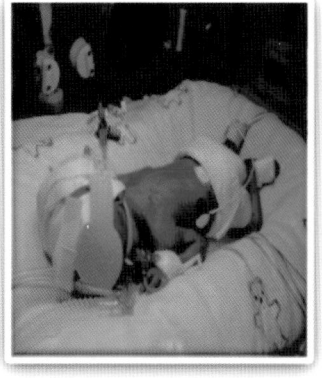

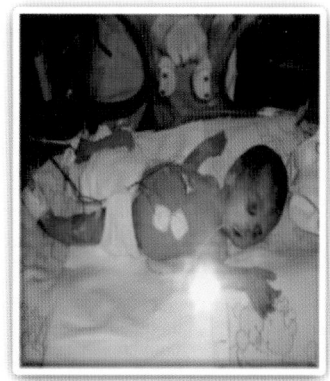

Leon, 14 months old

Leon, three years old

Lillie Murphy (28 weeks)

When my husband Keith and I found out we were expecting we were ecstatic. I had a son, Ben, who was born at term with no complications so I assumed this pregnancy would follow suit. Unfortunately, from the very onset this pregnancy was very different. From 13 weeks I was monitored for high blood pressure, and from 18 weeks for threatened eclampsia. I was monitored by my GP on a weekly basis. I knew Lillie was going to be born early; however, I didn't expect that she would be born at 28 weeks.

During a routine check in the Rotunda Hospital in Dublin, two days after Christmas, I was told I would be admitted. The baby was measuring small for her dates and there was some concern. The next few days passed in a blur of heart traces on Lillie, ultrasound scans and general tests. The hospital discovered there was very little amniotic fluid surrounding Lillie and that the blood was flowing backwards through the cord. I was given steroid injections to help develop her lungs.

Our micro-baby made her grand entrance into the world on New Year's Day. From that day on, our lives took a different direction. We were to spend the next 10 weeks by her incubator in the NICU willing our daughter to get stronger so we could bring her home, as well as trying to spend time with our son who was at home. From the time Lillie was born she was a trooper. She came into the world 12 weeks early, by emergency Caesarean section, weighing 0.69 kg (1 lb 7 oz). Throughout the procedure I was a wreck. The fear of the unknown outcome for my precious baby greatly outweighed any fear of the operating table. After she was delivered she was wrapped in what looked like a sandwich bag to maintain her body temperature. We got a glimpse of our precious daughter before she was whisked to the NICU. Upon her arrival she was ventilated straight away. However, after only nine hours of ventilation, she was extubated and put on CPAP. Even at such an early age she was a little fighter with determination.

From the beginning Lillie thrived. We became familiar with our surroundings and began to feel at ease. I stopped jumping every time a monitor beeped and gradually became accustomed to the many bradycardias and apnoeas she would have. I spent my days expressing milk and watching Lillie in her incubator, waiting for the precious moments when I could take her out for kangaroo care. Even mundane jobs such as a nappy change or feeding Lillie from a 1-ml syringe became a high point. After two weeks in NICU she was moved into special care. The jubilation of the moment was unreal. However, it was short-lived. Two days later, Lillie deteriorated dramatically. She was critically ill, her seemingly lifeless body a deathly shade of grey. These were some of the hardest hours of our lives. She was ventilated again and given high-dose antibiotics. We were told the next eight hours were life-threatening. Thankfully she pulled through, and we subsequently found out she had a serious blood infection which could have killed her. She stayed in intensive care for another three weeks and regained her strength before being moved back to SCBU.

When she got to SCBU she thrived once again. She began feeding from a bottle and eventually came off CPAP. Lillie was now breathing completely unaided. Her weight was creeping up slowly yet steadily; we were heading for home. Until, one day, our plans changed again. Lillie got Group B streptococcal septicaemia and was put on high-dose antibiotics. This changed our plans slightly as she had to stay in hospital until the course was finished. Luckily she was stronger this time and better able to deal with the infection.

Sixty-nine days after she made her dramatic entrance, Lillie was discharged from hospital, weighing 2.07 kg (4 lb 6 oz).

During her time in NICU and SCBU, Lillie had four blood transfusions for anaemia, ROP grade 2, which self-resolved, and two serious blood infections. She was born with a cyst on her ovary and a duplex kidney (one of her kidneys is split into two separate units). She is now thriving and a happy 18-month-old. She fought hard to be here with us today, and we owe an awful lot to the doctors and nurses who helped us get Lillie home. We are very proud of our little miracle. She is the light of our lives and is doted on by her big brother Ben.

Photographs of Lillie Murphy.

Lillie, minutes old

Lillie, three weeks old in her first dress

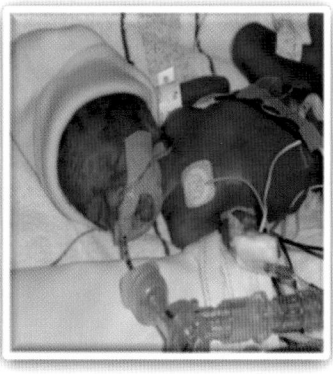

Lillie, meeting her brother Ben, eight weeks old

Lillie, 18 months old

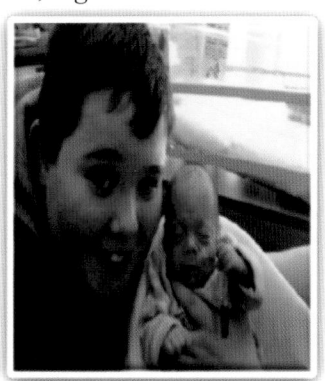

Lily Mary Reilly (32 weeks)

We found out on our honeymoon that we were expecting our second baby. When I was 30 weeks, my husband was in work and my two-year-old son was having a bad night. I leant into his cot and felt a pop.

The next day in hospital I got injections to help speed up the growth of the baby's lungs. Two weeks later, I got this sudden sharp pain and started bleeding. I was admitted to hospital. The next day, during a scan, I was getting pains, but was told I was not in labour. But the pains came on so strong and were coming so fast. I prayed to my Nanny Mary and told myself I wasn't in labour. One of the women in my room must have called the nurse because she told me to ring my husband and tell him I was going to the labour ward and to get in as soon as he could. When my husband arrived, the nurse told us there was nothing to worry about. I was fully dilated at 11.30 p.m. that night, and a minute later my baby girl arrived. She was 1.93 kg (4 lb 4 oz). We called her Lily Mary Reilly, she was beautiful, and I got to hold her before she was taken to the NICU.

After a quick sleep and shower, I went to see her. She was so tiny, all the beeps and wires scared me. I just wanted to kiss and hold her. The next day my son, Keegan, and my husband visited. It was hard trying to explain to my son that he had a sister but that he couldn't see her. The next day I was allowed go home. Leaving Lily broke my heart. Four days after she was born we got to hold her, it was magical. Lily went from strength to strength, each day was exciting to see how she was doing.

We read all the other baby cards and stories on the walls in the hospital. They gave us hope and made us smile. The doctor told us Lily would be able to go home on 31 October. We couldn't get her out of the hospital fast enough, just in case they changed their minds. The first time Keegan saw his sister he poked her nose and since then has become the best big brother. We are so lucky with Lily. She is the family's little Polly Pocket.

Photographs of Lily Mary Reilly.

Lily, just born

Lily and Daddy, aged three weeks

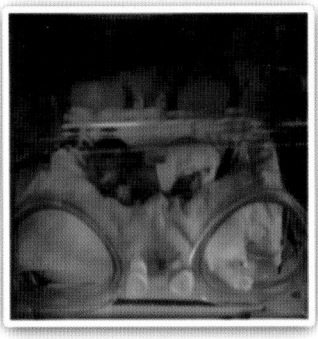

Lily's christening, aged 18 weeks and 4 days

Lily, aged nine months

Lucy Margaret Pollock (32 weeks)

We had no idea what was ahead of us when we arrived at Our Lady of Lourdes hospital in Drogheda, after my waters broke. I was 32 weeks pregnant with our first baby. Nineteen hours after arriving at the hospital, our little girl Lucy Margaret was born, weighing 1.79 kg (3 lb 15 oz). I remember very little of the birth or the first couple of times I saw Lucy. I still rely on photos and my husband filling me in on some details.

Lucy's first night was comfortable, and the neonatal staff said she was holding her own for now. The next day it all seemed so different; she was on CPAP. The staff informed us they were waiting on the result of a chest X-ray and blood gas before they could comment any further on her condition. That afternoon I sat on the postnatal ward with three other mothers and newborns trying to hand-express my breastmilk. All the other mothers were poring over their new bundles with joy, whilst all I could see was a photo of Lucy that the nurse had taken for me sitting in the empty cot beside me.

Later that same evening we got a call to return to the NICU. We were shocked to see that Lucy had been ventilated as a result of RDS. Her X-ray and blood gases showed signs that she was struggling, and we were then told the next 48 hours were critical. Lucy was three days old when I got discharged home. It broke our hearts leaving her behind. There were baby cards, flowers and balloons in the house, but it was too hard to look at them even though I know people meant well. They just seemed inappropriate at the time. We had very little sleep at home as I had to express every three hours and bring the milk to the NICU every day. Jason, my husband, had to return to work the following Monday as his leave had not been booked off for another two months. The staff in the hospital advised him to continue working until Lucy was home as there was very little he could do while she was in hospital. We worked out a rota where I travelled up to Drogheda every morning until six or seven in the evening and Jason drove from Dublin after work to see her. Over the next few days and weeks she required treatment for various conditions, from apnoea to jaundice. She had problems maintaining her body temperature and blood sugars and received TPN for nutrition until she was able to tolerate tube-feeds. Her feet and hands were black and blue from the lines and tests.

The first day we felt like real parents was on the fifth day, when we got to hold Lucy and practise skin-to-skin, or kangaroo, care. Over the next week or so her condition was volatile. Just after two weeks she appeared to be turning a corner, when the ventilator and CPAP were slowly weaned off and the volume of her tube-feeding was increasing. Soon after this we received some bad news. A brain scan showed Lucy was suffering from a bleed. The consultant told us there was a chance of cerebral palsy and development delay. We remained optimistic, and every day Lucy got stronger. Finally, after four weeks, she was discharged. She was 2.04 kg (4 lb 8 oz), on two-hourly feeds and on an apnoea monitor.

The next few years were tough. Lucy suffered with reflux for nine months and developed asthma. Further brain scans showed the bleed had stopped and was reabsorbed but would still need monitoring until pre-school or school age. She had a lowered resistance to infections and was constantly on antibiotics. She spent her first years mostly indoors and away from crowds as advised by her consultants. She suffered urinary-tract infections for 18 months, and temperatures over 38 degrees sent her into convulsions.

At the time of writing this, Lucy is three years old and doing great. There are no signs of cerebral palsy, but she still attends the clinic every six months for check-ups. She has been discharged from the urology clinic, and there are no signs of further kidney damage. Developmentally she has caught up with her peers and is just a little lighter and slimmer. Lucy attends a local crèche part-time and enjoys the socialisation. She is a big sister to Ethan and Levi. Being parents of a premature baby has been a challenge, but one which we have overcome, and we will never forget how Lucy fought to be here.

Photographs of Lucy Margaret Pollock.

Lucy at three days, fighting

Lucy, one week

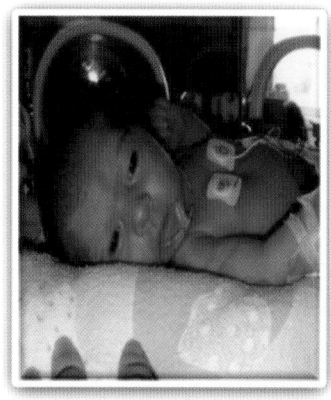

Lucy enjoying kangaroo care with Mummy

A happy, healthy Lucy today, aged three

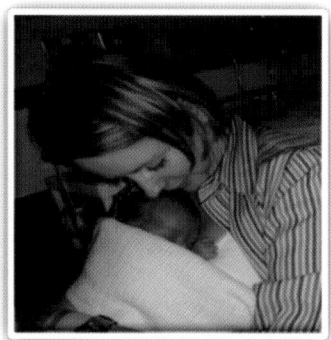

Max James Huse and Molly Ann Huse (32 weeks)

We were delighted to be expecting twins, a girl and a boy. At our 20-week scan, the sonographer was checking twin 1, then moved to check twin 2. She went quiet and was measuring over and over again. I asked her was everything OK, and she replied that she had to leave but would be back. When she returned she asked us to wait to meet a specialist, which we did. She told us that twin 2's femur had not grown since the 16-week scan and that his bowel was a light colour.

We had to go back for a scan every week to keep an eye on the twins. Over the next few weeks more problems arose with twin 2, his placenta was only working at half-rate, and he had reverse flow. We were then told that twin 2 would not survive the pregnancy. My parents lost a premature triplet when I was four. His name was Malcolm John, and I prayed to him every night to protect the twins. We decided to name the babies. We wanted to make a closer bond with them. Molly Ann was named after both our grandmothers. Max means little fighter, and we gave him James as a middle name, so he would have the same initials as Malcolm John.

At week 26, I was admitted to hospital with pre-eclampsia. I had a mini-scan every three hours and was given steroid injections to develop the babies' lungs. After four days I was allowed home. I had to attend the hospital every week for blood tests and to monitor my blood pressure. I got to know all the nurses who were taking care of me, and they got to know me well. Each time I had a mini-scan they would say, 'Let's see how Max and Molly are doing.' It really meant so much to me having nurses around that remembered their names.

At week 30, Max was measuring the size of a 22-week-gestation baby. This is when the medical staff said it was not looking good for him, but he was trying his hardest to hold on. Molly was doing great and thriving. Then, at the 32-week scan, the doctor informed us that he was going to do a Caesarean section within an hour. In the operating theatre there were 18 staff members. Martin, my partner, held my hand throughout the C-section. Five minutes into the C-section, I heard a cry. It was Molly. She was born weighing 1.5 kg (3 lb 8 oz). The room went silent. After a few minutes I heard a very faint cry. All I can say is it sounded like a squeaky toy. Max was born weighing 0.82 kg (1 lb 13 oz). The paediatrician then brought Molly over for us. That's when I started panicking about my Max.

I was then brought into the recovery room. The nurses rang the NICU for me every hour to see how the twins are. After a day I got to meet them. The staff were really helpful. The minute I went in a staff member came over to me and brought me to the twins and went through what had happened when I was in the recovery room. She told me that Max was on a ventilator for the first six hours but that he was breathing all on his own now. Molly was doing great. She was under a UV light for jaundice. The nurse then took Max out of the incubator and placed him in my arms. I realised how lucky I was to have both babies alive.

After six days in hospital I was discharged although I didn't want to go home; I didn't want to leave the twins. The last night of my stay I went up to the NICU. When I walked in one of the nurses had Molly and was giving her a bottle and singing lullabies to her. I knew Max and Molly were in safe hands.

After three weeks, Molly was discharged. We put her into the incubator with Max to say goodbye for now. The staff usually gave them about 20 minutes together each day, and Molly was forever pulling at Max's feeding tube. It was hard bringing Molly home and leaving Max behind.

When Max was six weeks old, he was discharged. Molly and Max were finally and rightfully reunited. Martin and I wondered if they would recognise each other after the separation. We placed them beside each other. The first thing Molly did was grasp Max's nose. I never laughed so much. We all said that Molly remembered Max in the incubator and was looking for the tube. It's now 11 months since their birth, and they are doing amazing. We are so proud of them.

Photographs of Max James Huse and Molly Ann Huse.

Max, three weeks old

Molly, three weeks

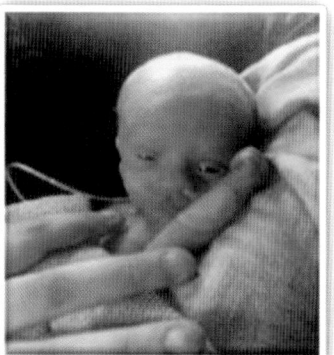
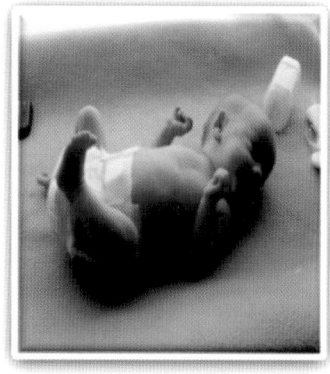

Molly, going home before Max

Max and Molly, aged one, in their first pair of Levi's

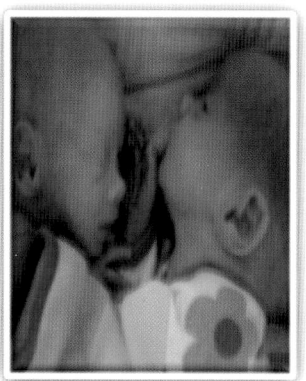

Mia-Bella McGarr (27 weeks)

On 8 October I was 27 weeks pregnant. I knew something was not right as my body was so swollen I could barely fit in my clothes or shoes. After a stressful day in work I went to the chemist to get my blood pressure checked. The pharmacist took one look at the monitor and told me to get myself to hospital straight away. I headed off to hospital and was admitted immediately. I was given steroid injections within an hour of arriving at the hospital to develop the baby's lungs. I knew from that moment that I was no longer going to have a normal pregnancy.

I was diagnosed with severe pre-eclampsia. I was put on medication to try to stabilise my blood pressure. Three days later, on 11 October, at 11.00 p.m., a team of doctors came to my bed, started packing up my belongings, pulling off my clothes and explaining that I was in danger and that they had no choice but to deliver our baby via emergency Caesarean section. I was in complete shock and absolutely terrified. I could not believe what was happening, it just seemed to happen so quickly.

I was taken to the HDU where doctors tried to stabilise my blood pressure before surgery. At 1.52 a.m. the following morning our amazing little girl Mia-Bella was born, weighing 0.99 kg (2 lb 3 oz). I will never forget the relief we felt when we heard her tiny little cry for the first time. The paediatric doctors took her away immediately to work on her. It was heartbreaking having her taken away from me without being able to hold her. Everything is such a blur after this as I was taken to recovery and Mia-Bella to the NICU. The following day, I was brought up to the NICU in a wheelchair. I was in agony but was determined to see my baby.

It was another three days before I would be able to hold my baby. Even with her breathing tubes and IV drips still attached, words will never do justice to the feeling of holding her for the first time. Mia-Bella was ventilated for 24 hours and spent seven weeks on BiPAP and CPAP. She encountered a few problems along the way. She had a PDA, which thankfully closed first with the ibuprofen medication. This meant she did not require heart surgery. She also had tachycardia (accelerated heart rate), bradycardia, apnoea, an inguinal hernia (which corrected itself), fluid on her lungs and a blood transfusion.

Despite all the complications she had, Mia-Bella was a feisty little girl, and she bravely fought everything that happened to her. She was released from hospital after 64 days on 15 December, just in time for her first Christmas. We were delighted her first Christmas would be spent at home with all of her family. It was the most amazing feeling to walk out the doors of the Rotunda Hospital in Dublin with our little miracle.

Mia-Bella came home on an apnoea monitor and diuretics to help keep her system flushed so that fluid didn't build up on her lungs again. She was doing great for the first three weeks. Then, one morning, at 5.00 a.m., her apnoea monitor kept sounding. Before this it had gone off only a handful of times so I knew something was wrong. I could see that her breathing was irregular so we brought her straight to Temple Street Children's University Hospital in Dublin. On arriving at the hospital she was immediately put on oxygen as her oxygen levels were low. It was terrifying not knowing what was wrong with my baby. She was moved to isolation on precautionary antibiotics and oxygen, and she had a feeding tube inserted as she was too lethargic to drink her bottles. She had X-rays, cranial ultrasounds and spinal taps, but everything appeared to be normal. Thankfully it turned out to be a viral infection, and Mia-Bella was discharged after five days.

Mia-Bella is now a healthy nine-month-old. She has just mastered sitting up on her own and rolling over. She is an inquisitive happy little baby who never sits still. She brings so much happiness into our lives. I am forever grateful to all the doctors and nurses in the Rotunda because they made Mia-Bella's homecoming possible.

Photographs of Mia-Bella McGarr.

Mia-Bella, 12 hours old

Mia-Bella, four days old, first cuddle with Mammy

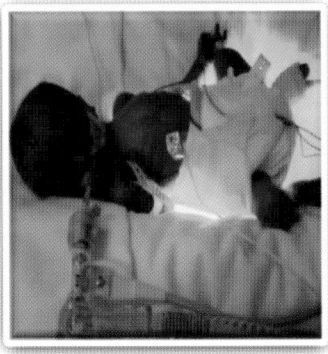

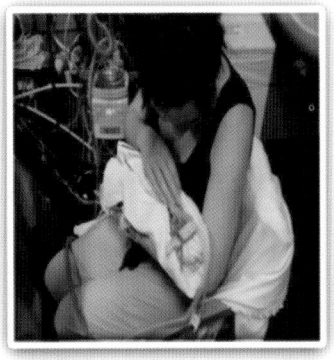

Mia-Bella now

Mia-Bella now, nine months old

Mollie Mullen (26 weeks)

Baby Mollie was born at 1.43 p.m. on 15 January in the Rotunda Hospital in Dublin. A gorgeous baby girl, just what we had always dreamed of, but never in our wildest dreams did we think she would arrive three months earlier than expected. Until a few days before Mollie's birth my pregnancy had been quite normal. On 11 January, I visited my GP for a routine check-up but my blood pressure was noted to be elevated. The doctor, suspecting that I had pre-eclampsia, sent me immediately to Daisy Hill Hospital in Newry. Over the next two days my blood pressure continued to rise dangerously high, and I was transferred to the Rotunda Hospital. We didn't know a lot about pre-eclampsia, and I was shocked when we were told that our baby might have to be delivered much earlier than we had anticipated. Four nights later, at 26 weeks, Mollie was delivered by emergency Caesarean section, weighing 0.65 kg (1 lb 7 oz). The consultant visited later that day and told us how critical her situation was and that she only had a 50–50 chance of survival.

I saw Mollie for the first time the following day in the NICU, and I could not believe how helpless and tiny she looked. It was a tough day, but my husband and I agreed to be strong and tried not to get too upset. The NICU was a very scary place, and it was difficult to see our little baby dependent on so much medical technology and expertise. We worried about every sound the various monitors and machines made and hoped Mollie wasn't in any difficulty. The unit's head sister warned us that we had a roller-coaster ride ahead of us, and that was certainly the case.

We received good news that Mollie's brain scans were clear and that there was no sign of any bleeding. At the same time, Mollie's lungs were underdeveloped, and she was relying on a ventilator to assist her breathing. She required numerous blood transfusions as she was as yet unable to make her own red blood cells. One Sunday, we met a surgeon from Our Lady's Children's Hospital in Crumlin who had been called in to carry out a procedure to put a drain into Mollie's bowel. The doctors feared that she might develop NEC, but luckily this problem self-resolved. Mollie also had a PDA. A large duct was placing too much pressure on her heart which meant it could not pump enough blood around her body. This made it impossible for Mollie to breathe on her own and she needed to be ventilated. Everything had a knock-on effect. Because of the medication that was needed to heal Mollie's bowel disorder, her heart condition could not be treated medicinally and so the duct would have to be closed surgically. The operation in Crumlin was successful, and Mollie was finally moved out of NICU and into special care, which came as a huge relief.

After a few days in special care Mollie was like a different baby. She made great strides on the CPAP and was steadily putting on weight. On 3 February, Mollie was transferred from the Rotunda to Our Lady of Lourdes Hospital in Drogheda. This was an emotional day, and we had mixed feelings about leaving the specialist care at the Rotunda, but it was more practical to have Mollie closer to home.

The transition went smoothly. Mollie was doing well on CPAP and was being tube-fed. However, she was diagnosed with ROP and had to be transferred to the NMH for both laser and surgery on her eyes. This was incredibly nerve-wracking. Once again we had to put our trust in the amazing medical professionals and hope everything would be alright. Mollie's progress gathered momentum. Before long she could breathe unaided and had started to bottle-feed. One week later, on

Easter Sunday, after the longest 100 days of our lives, our baby girl (weighing 2.95 kg [6 lb 8 oz]) was coming home at last.

Mollie is now six months old, three months corrected, and doing everything she should be at this stage. She is such a beautiful and happy little baby. I know our journey has only started and we have a long way to go, but all it takes is one little smile to melt both our hearts and make it all worthwhile. We got here through positive thinking and the love and support from our family and friends. We would like to thank our loved ones from the bottom of our hearts for being there through the tough days.

Photographs of Mollie Mullen.

Mollie, one day old

Mollie, nine days old

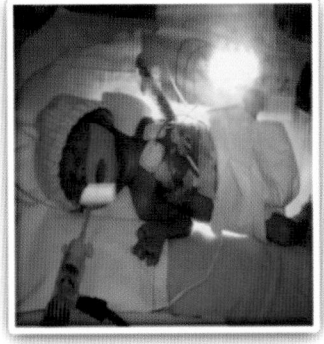

Mollie, four months old

Mollie, four months old

Molly Dowdall Killeen (26 weeks)

When we announced my pregnancy to our families on Christmas Day, we didn't expect to have to announce the birth of our baby girl less than three months later, on Saint Patrick's Day. My pregnancy was so short that few people even saw the tiny bump. My pregnancy was also difficult. I was sick from week 6 and felt unrelentingly exhausted. In mid-March I was feeling particularly dismal as I attended a routine check-up, and it was discovered that I had a chest, throat and kidney infection. Due to a high temperature I was admitted and started on a course of antibiotics.

During this stay, a scan revealed a problem. Molly was very small for her gestation, and she was surrounded by very little amniotic fluid. A decidedly handsome and worried obstetrician was dispatched to break the terrible news to us, that she would be delivered a week later. I was immediately started on a course of steroids in an attempt to quicken the development of Molly's lungs, and we were left trying to absorb this overwhelming news. While trying to remain positive we were preparing ourselves and our families for difficult news.

In some ways I am thankful that Molly didn't give us much time to dwell on the frightful situation in which we found ourselves. Two days later I went into spontaneous labour. Not having gotten past week 24 in my pregnancy books, I was oblivious to what could potentially be ahead of us, and for the rest of my life I will thank my lucky stars that I was in the Rotunda Hospital and not sitting at home at the time, the consequences of which are unthinkable.

Molly was delivered by emergency Caesarean section at just 26 weeks, weighing 0.62 kg (1 lb 6 oz). After a quick 'hello' to her startled mother she was wheeled past her father who was waiting in the corridor and whisked away to the NICU, where she was to spend the next 16 weeks. During this time she was treated for ROP, apnoea, anaemia, jaundice, CLD, a bleed on her brain and an umbilical hernia. She had several infections and three blood transfusions. Molly endured continuous medical intervention and intrusion, pain, discomfort and distressing procedures on a daily basis.

Considering a baby at this gestation is not expecting to be touched, I always noticed how obviously uncomfortable Molly was even being stroked gently by us or her grandparents. I can never imagine how horrific this time must have been for her. The shock of all this intervention must have been horrendous for her.

It was three weeks before I got to hold Molly, and it was a nerve-wracking occasion. Her little legs were no bigger than my index finger, and she weighed virtually nothing. She was only in my arms a minute or so when she stopped breathing. The alarms sent two nurses running, and unfortunately Molly had to be returned to her incubator. It was a day or two after this event that the decision was taken to send Molly to Our Lady's Children's Hospital in Dublin for a PDA cardiac operation. We were assured by the hospital staff of the high success rate for this operation, but nothing could alleviate the worry and distress that we were feeling at the time. No one can lift the unease and anxiety off your shoulders, and you have no choice but to put your faith in the hands of the surgeon and wait patiently while your child's life hangs in the balance.

Molly really turned a corner after that, and within a week she was taken off her ventilator and moved to CPAP. The next 12 weeks were spent sitting, watching and waiting; each day checking how many grams she had lost or gained; waiting to hear if there were any setbacks or achievements, no matter how small; listening to the sounds of the alarms; watching newer babies arrive and older ones leave; making friends, swapping stories and prodding nurses for hints and tips on surviving the homecoming of a premature baby. They were very long days.

Molly was breathing unassisted for two weeks before she came home, just five days after her due date. Our house was filled with the family, friends and neighbours who had waited four long months to meet her. It was a very happy day and one that will remain with me for ever. The resilience and endurance that Molly showed in those early days is still in evidence today and hopefully will remain with her for ever. She proves incessantly that people were not wrong when they tried to reassure us that she was 'a little fighter'. She is a happy, healthy little girl who loves a good argument, meeting new people and bouncing on her trampoline. We know how very lucky we are to have her.

Photographs of Molly Dowdall Killeen.

Molly, aged 10 days

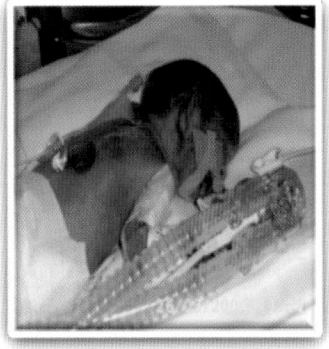

Molly, aged two months

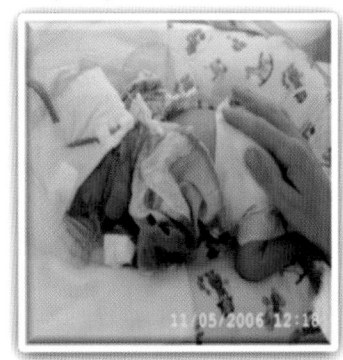

Molly, aged six months

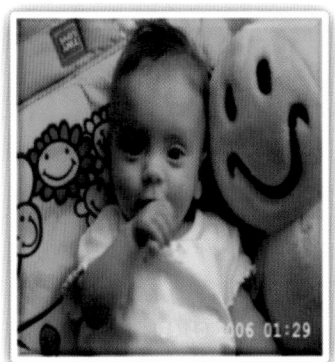

Molly, aged five

Nicole O'Neill (27 weeks)

Our daughter Nicole was born in the NMH in Dublin on 29 May at 27 weeks and 3 days' gestation. On the night of 18 May I had a bleed and decided to go into hospital to get checked out. When the doctor examined me he told me I was a few centimetres dilated, that he could see the bulging membrane and that my baby was going to be born within a few hours. I was only 26 weeks, so panic ran through me worrying was my baby going to survive. They gave me the first injection of steroids to help her lungs and said I may not get the chance to receive the second injection. I spent the whole night and the following morning in the labour ward. My waters were still intact so the doctors were able to administer the second steroid injection and I was put on bed rest in the hospital.

I remained on bed rest for 10 more days until 29 May when my waters broke. I had to have an emergency section as the baby was lying transverse (sideways). Nicole was born weighing 1.36 kg (3 lb). She was transferred to NICU 2, and I got to see her a few hours later. The first time I saw my tiny little baby lying in the incubator with all the wires and tubes coming from her was very hard. I felt numb and helpless as I couldn't hold my baby like all new mothers do. As the days went on it got easier to accept, and I was able to hold her and do kangaroo care and to tube-feed her. Some days were good, and some were very hard. It felt like I was on a roller-coaster. During Nicole's stay, she had three blood transfusions, a PDA, which has since closed, and a small hole in her heart. She was also diagnosed with laryngomalacia (floppy windpipe).

Nicole spent 47 days in hospital, and we finally got to take our little princess home on 15 July. While it was the happiest day of our lives, we were still nervous. As the days and weeks went by, it was amazing to see our little girl get bigger and stronger. She is now a healthy, happy little 13-month-old girl. She was a little slower than a full-term baby to sit, crawl, etc., but she got there in her own time and still has that little fight in her that she had when she was born.

Photographs of Nicole O'Neill.

Nicole, one hour old

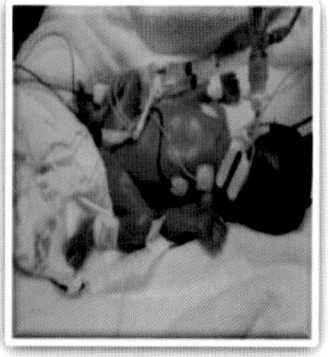

Nicole, three days old

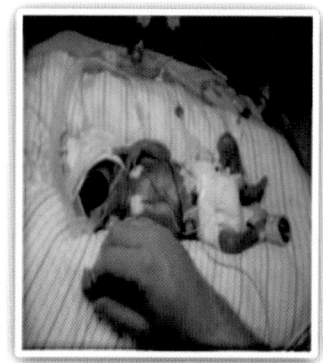

Nicole, five months old

Nicole on her first birthday

Orla Marie Carr (27 weeks)

On Saturday, 13 November, I left home in Limerick to travel to Kilkenny for a night away with the girls. At 3.00 a.m. I started to feel unwell and to get pains. When I reached the hospital I was in labour and was given steroid injections for the baby's lungs. I was put on a drip to stop my labour. The following morning I was moved to Waterford Regional Hospital to be near the NICU. Here I met up with my husband JJ and my mother. On Monday I received the next steroid injection.

On Tuesday morning things started to go wrong. I was rushed for an emergency Caesarean section, and Orla Marie Carr was born at 1.00 p.m., at 27 weeks and 4 days' gestation, weighing 1.39 kg (3 lb 1 oz). JJ said he will never forget the first time he saw her in the doctor's arms, so tiny, so fragile. I didn't see her until the following day. It was so upsetting. Nothing could have prepared us for the shock of seeing Orla in the NICU for the first time.

The first week in the hospital went fairly well. Orla was gradually being weaned off the ventilator. Her weight dropped to 1.16 kg (2 lb 9 oz) and her glucose levels dropped. As her mother, I wasn't able to do much for her, but I expressed my breastmilk, which they started giving her at a rate of 0.5 ml per hour. Seven nights after Orla was born it was time for me to leave the hospital. Going home without my baby was very hard. We were very lucky to find somewhere to stay, five minutes from the hospital with a fabulous woman called Tina, who gave us a room in her house, and this was to become home for the next seven weeks.

The time came for JJ to go back to work, but we had great support from our family. Orla was taken off the ventilator after eight nights. Luckily I had been given steroid injections to help develop her lungs as, after this, Orla didn't need assisted breathing during her stay in the NICU. After four weeks she became jaundiced and was put under blue lights for two days.

Getting to hold Orla for the first time was a very precious moment. Simple things such as changing her nappy gave us time to bond with her. Helping look after her became part of our daily routine in the hospital. I was still expressing milk, but when the time came to feed her we decided to bottle-feed her EBM as this way we would know how much she had taken. The highlight of our week was when Orla got weighed. This would inevitably be followed by many phone calls and texts to tell people of her weight gain.

The next big move was to the isolation area, the last step before going home. Here Orla had a room of her own which was so quiet compared to the hustle and bustle of the NICU. At one point there was talk of moving back to Limerick but we decided to stay just in case the long journey adversely affected her health.

Leaving Orla in the hospital on Christmas Day was one of the hardest things we ever did, but the day came and went, and we moved on, knowing there would be many more Christmas Days to celebrate. On New Year's Eve we were told that Orla needed a blood transfusion, and it did her the power of good, as two days later we were told it was time to take her home. On Wednesday, 5 January, we left the hospital, and Orla now weighed 2.33 kg (5 lb 2 oz). This was a very happy day, with lots of celebrations.

The first few months at home were hard. Orla was poor to take her feeds; she suffered with reflux and colic so she cried a lot and didn't sleep much. This was a very stressful time but once she settled (at 11 months), life got much easier, and family life was great. We had to go back to Waterford for check-ups, but at the age of two we were told that Orla was doing so well that we didn't have to go back any more. Orla does not suffer from any ill effects as a result of her premature birth apart from being very thin, but as a girl I'm sure this will make her happy for years to come. Orla is now a beautiful, bright, loving six-year-old, and every day she brings us much happiness. We are blessed to have her in our lives.

Photographs of Orla Marie Carr.

Orla, three hours old

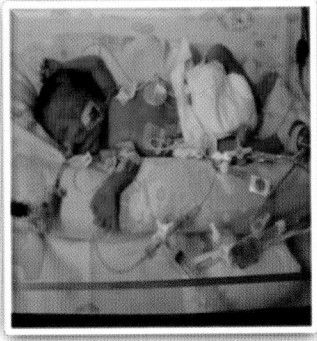

Orla's first Christmas

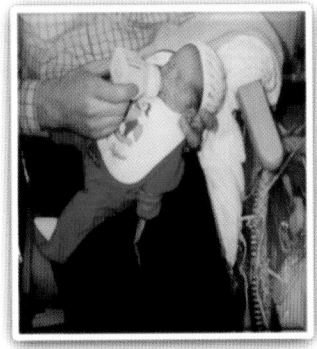

Orla aged two, first Trick or Treat

Orla, aged six with brother Jack

Robin Cotter (28 weeks)

After a troubled pregnancy, our first little boy, Brody, was born sleeping on 3 September. We were both nervous and excited to discover I was pregnant again in the November of the following year. A couple of weeks later, on 31 December, I started to bleed and was gripped with fear. A scan revealed that a miscarriage was inevitable. Our world fell apart, but two weeks later a follow-up scan revealed that the baby was still alive and growing. The bleeding settled down, and my beautiful bump began to grow, as did our hope. But at 22 weeks the bleeding started again, which is when things started to go wrong with Brody, so the feeling of déjà-vu was overwhelming. I was sent home to rest and was monitored carefully. At 26 weeks I spent two weeks in hospital where I received steroid injections to help our baby's lungs develop, in case of an early delivery. When I got to 28 weeks (the gestation at which Brody was born), every movement from then on was a bonus. But our joy didn't last very long, and the next day I woke with pains and knew instinctively that something wasn't right. We rushed to the hospital where I was examined by the medical team and my waters broke. It was then I realised that I was about to become a mammy again. It all happened super-fast: our little boy Robin came screaming into the world on 19 May and our lives changed for ever.

Robin was tiny but alive, and I felt such a mixture of emotions as he was taken away to the NICU. We were given a picture of him, hooked up to all sorts of machines with tubes and wires sticking out of him. It was awful to see him like that, but I was told he was doing really well. He weighed 1.36 kg (3 lb) and was breathing on his own with the help of CPAP. The first time I saw my boy properly was amazing.

The feeling of love I had for this tiny person was instant and all-consuming, and I knew everything would be OK so long as he was alive.

My first challenge was to express breastmilk. It was the strangest thing I have ever done, but it seemed to work. I was soon discharged and felt so torn leaving without my baby. The first time I held Robin I literally thought my heart would burst. He was amazing, covered in a soft down that felt like velvet, his tiny fingers holding onto me and his eyes looking up at me. He remained on CPAP and was treated for jaundice. He started losing weight, his breathing dipped a lot, and he picked up an infection which required treatment with antibiotics. But, soon enough, he began to turn a corner and started to put on weight.

After a couple of weeks, Robin was promoted to the SCBU, one step closer to home. I spent each day visiting him, timing it so that I could express milk and feed him when I arrived. We practised kangaroo care every day, whereby I would gently place Robin down my top, skin to skin. He loved it, his breathing never dipped while we were together. At this point Robin was still being fed with a nasal tube but I really wanted to breastfeed. It was really difficult to begin with but we thankfully got the hang of it. I am so glad we persevered as it was a wonderful bonding experience. Then we finally progressed from SCBU to the nursery, the last stop before home.

We got to bring our little superhero home, after almost nine weeks. We didn't know whether to laugh or cry, terrified and elated at the same time. It was so strange to not have anyone watching us, no machines, no beeping, just us and our boy. That first night at home was terrible, but we got through it. I slept when he did, fed on demand, gradually stopped expressing so that he was exclusively breastfed and just enjoyed every second of our time together. I never imagined I could be happy again after Brody – never completely happy but as close as we were ever going to get. Robin used to lie in my arms and watch the ceiling, and I knew his big brother was there, watching over him. Robin is doing well. He is such a little character and has the best chuckle that comes straight from his belly. He is the light of our lives, and not a day goes by without me thinking how truly blessed we are to have him.

Photographs of Robin Cotter.

Robin in the NICU

Robin being fed

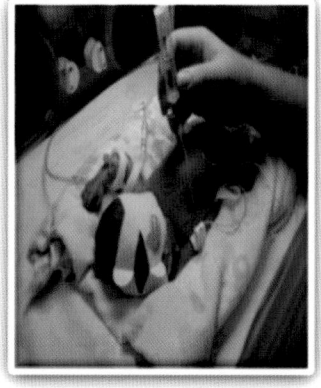

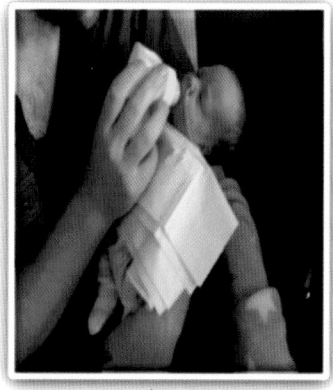

Robin having cuddle time

Robin having fun

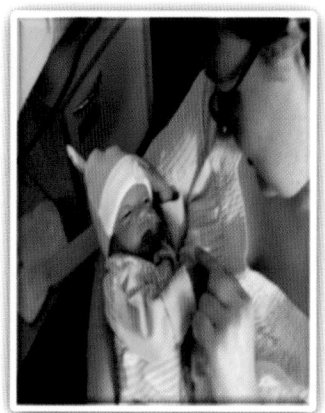

Ruairí Craig (25 weeks)

On Wednesday, 8 October, at 9.38 p.m., Ruairí was born in Mayo General Hospital. He was born at week 25 of pregnancy, weighing 0.81 kg (1 lb 13 oz). Ruairí's prognosis at birth wasn't good: the doctors worked on him for 20 minutes without a sustained response. We thought that he would not survive his early arrival as he would only take a single gasp of breath every five minutes and his heart rate was very low. The nurses dressed Ruairí in a tiny blue babygro and a woollen blue hat. My baby boy appeared so perfect but seemed so lifeless. Ruairí's dad and I, along with his grandparents and auntie, were left alone for what we thought would be the last few minutes of his life. After some time, Ruairí began to take more frequent gasps, and from that point onward everything changed. The doctors took Ruairí back into the SCBU where he then only required 50 per cent oxygen and was put on BiPAP. The doctors observed Ruairí overnight, and, like most parents of a premature baby, we could only look ahead an hour at a time.

The next day, Ruairí was transferred to the Rotunda Hospital in Dublin. The neonatal transport team came from Dublin to transfer him. It took four hours to prepare him as he had to be ventilated for the trip. The doctor and nurse who came to collect him had to observe him and ensure he was stable enough to travel. After all the checks, Ruairí was ready for the journey.

The nurse rang when they reached Dublin. Ruairí was settled, and everything was going well so far. The following Sunday my mother and I went to see him. We were so amazed at this tiny bundle who had fought so hard and who was continuously fighting to make it through. The next evening we were advised to come to the hospital as Ruairí was very ill with an infection and his outcome was uncertain. Ruairí's infection, which he had contracted *in utero*, and which had resulted in his premature birth, was deemed very serious. The following two weeks were almost unbearable. Ruairí was put on high ventilation as he had stopped breathing yet again. He required a blood transfusion, and his kidneys appeared to be failing as he hadn't passed any urine.

Thankfully, after about two and a half weeks, Ruairí's infection stabilised, and on 31 October I got to hold my precious baby for the first time. It was like nothing I had ever felt. He was so light you wouldn't know he was in your arms. Ruairí had many infections and blood transfusions over the next few weeks, but after 73 days of ventilation he was finally able for CPAP.

I was ecstatic my little miracle was getting stronger and stronger. Of course there were setbacks; for every one step forward he took five steps back. Finally, at Christmas time, after weeks of cycles on and off the ventilator, Ruairí came off the ventilator permanently. Also in December, Ruairí required laser treatment to his eyes twice. In January, Ruairí turned the corner; he was weaned off CPAP and eventually was transferred into a cot. A week later, the doctors decided that he was well enough to be transferred back to Mayo General Hospital.

Before his transfer, Ruairí underwent a hernia repair operation in Our Lady's Children's Hospital in Crumlin. Three weeks later, he had to return to Dublin for a second hernia operation on the opposite side of his groin. At this point, Ruairí's inability to feed adequately was the only obstacle preventing his discharge home, but with time and patience he started to feed, and on 11 March he was finally allowed to go home. After five months in hospital, Ruairí was home with his family.

Today, Ruairí is two years old. He has developmental delay and isn't walking or talking but is receiving assistance in these areas from health professionals. When he was a year and a half, Ruairí had a PEG feed inserted due to silent aspiration which had caused numerous chest infections and had resulted in several hospital admissions. Ruairí is a bubbly, happy child who loves to be stuck in the middle of all the fun with his Auntie Niamh and baby brother Fiachra. It has been an incredible roller-coaster journey for our family, one I could not have endured without the support of my mother and sisters. Ruairí has fought against the odds. He really is my fighting little miracle.

Photographs of Ruairí Craig.

Ruairí, four days old

Holding Ruairí, three weeks old

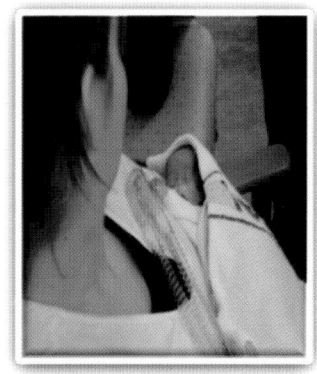

Ruairí, first time in a cot

Ruairí, aged two

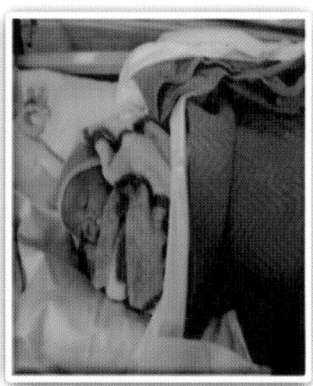

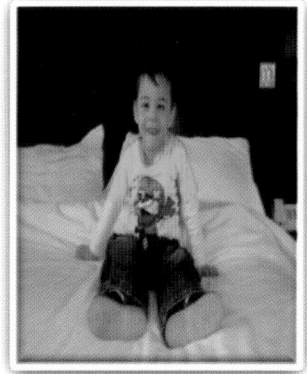

Ryan Scallan (30 weeks)

Our roller-coaster ride started on Monday, 6 August, 29 weeks' pregnant, when I was admitted to hospital with high blood pressure. Having received steroids for the baby's lungs I was discharged only to be admitted two days later by our GP who told my husband to go home and prepare a baby bag. We both looked at her as if she had two heads. During the night my blood pressure became increasingly high, and the following morning I was rushed from Wexford to CUMH's HDU where I was pumped with various drugs to attempt to stabilise my blood pressure.

A nurse sat my bedside all night monitoring my blood pressure and pumping more drugs into me. On Sunday, 12 August, a consultant came to see me, and it all became a blur once the word 'delivery' came into the conversation. I was prepared for emergency Caesarean section, and our little man Ryan was born at 12.24 p.m., weighing just 1.37 kg (3 lb). I remember hearing his first cry so well. The paediatric team attended to Ryan and whisked him off to ICU. Our little man had done so well from the start, only needing CPAP for 24 hours. I was brought back to the HDU, and that night the nurses wheeled me down in my bed to see Ryan for the first time. We were both confined to our beds at this stage and had no physical contact until the following evening.

The emotions over the next few days are indescribable. In comparison to other parents in ICU our story is not as tragic as some. It was very hard to witness the devastation other parents went through. I was discharged after a week and had to find an apartment to stay in, not knowing how long we were going to be there. After two weeks Ryan was transferred back to the SCBU in Wexford. This was the first time he became unstable, requiring both oxygen and caffeine for the first time. For the next four and a half weeks I spent my time sitting by his side and at home sitting with a breast pump. We had the common difficulties with jaundice, feeding and infections. After six and a half weeks Ryan was discharged, and I was filled with fear and excitement about how to look after a premature baby. Ryan is nearly four now and, thank God, has no health issues from being a premmie.

Photographs of Ryan Scallan.

Ryan, aged four hours old

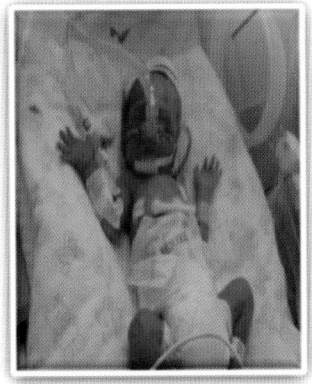

Ryan, one day old

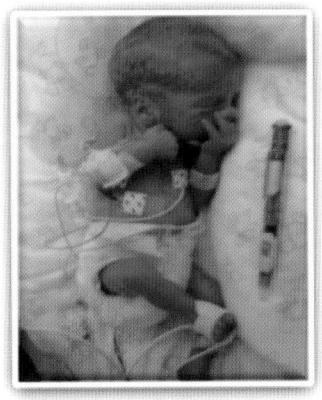

Ryan, aged one and a half

Ryan, aged three

⊂⊃

Samuel Heagney (30 weeks)

Samuel was born in the NMH, Holles Street, at 6.44 p.m. on 1 June 2010, after an emergency Caesarean section due to placental abruption. He weighed just 1.67 kg (3 lb 11 oz). His arrival was a shock. His sister Lauren and brothers Hugh and Harry had all been born after their due date, and we expected it would be the same with Samuel. His due date was 3 August, and we had joked we would call him 'Hat-Trick' if he was 10 days late as he would then have shared his birthday with Hugh and Harry, who were born on 13 August one year apart. But alone he now stands after arriving into our lives so early.

It all happened so quickly. His birth took place less than three hours after the emergency had started while I was at work at Dublin Airport. The night of his birth was very strange. Given his rushed arrival, I only saw him for a few moments before he was taken up to NICU, and I had only a photo on his daddy's mobile phone before I finally got to see him properly the following day. It was an overwhelming experience to see him then, as there were so many incubators and monitors in the unit. Samuel looked tiny. He was having help with his breathing and was on CPAP, and the first time I got to hold him was very emotional.

I had expressed milk for Samuel, and he was also on formula. At first he was doing really well and was moved to NICU2. A nurse described this as 'a promotion', which we were thrilled to hear. We had also been encouraged by the corridor wall in Unit 8 where so many heart-warming stories of other babies had been pinned up for worried parents to read. This was very useful to us given that we had been so used to our other pregnancies going the full term.

I got to go home from hospital the following Sunday, and while it was very difficult leaving Samuel behind, we knew he was in the best place possible. Our visit the next day, the bank-holiday Monday, when the women's mini-marathon was taking place in the streets nearby, was also positive. However, there was bad news on the Tuesday. We were told that Samuel was now very sick as he had developed a life-threatening condition called NEC. He was taken off his feeds and put on TPN and a mixture of antibiotics. His bowel was also X-rayed at regular intervals because if it perforated he would need surgery.

That Tuesday night Samuel was given a blood transfusion, but the following day the doctor informed us that his bowel appeared to have perforated. She also prepared us for the worst, and Samuel was baptised before being transferred to Our Lady's Children's Hospital in Crumlin. There was some good news there, though. Following further tests, we were assured that while Samuel was very sick his bowel hadn't perforated, and he was to be transferred back to Holles Street on the Friday. However, the news that we feared wasn't long in coming as his bowel soon perforated and he was whisked back to Crumlin on the Saturday for life-saving surgery during which the diseased part of his bowel was removed. A stoma was brought out through his abdomen, which meant that he would need to wear a bag to pass faeces into until the stoma was reversed.

The next few days were spent anxiously waiting for Samuel to poo through the stoma, which would demonstrate that the operation had been a success. The intensive-care team at Crumlin Paediatric ICU 1 looked after him marvellously, and after spending a further few days in a general ward he was moved back to Holles Street, which was to become a home from home in the weeks that followed. It was here that we had to learn how to care for his ileostomy bag, putting it on and removing it, a tricky process that we had to do every two days or whenever it leaked, but we eventually got the hang of it.

With his health continuing to improve, Samuel was allowed to come home with us on 8 July, which was such a relief. He was still tiny, but while it was initially quite scary for us having to care for him on our own, we got by. Every hospital appointment we had to bring him to provided further hope that everything was going to work out fine as every medic we encountered said that Samuel was progressing all the time.

Since the stoma reversal Samuel's development has been fantastic. He took his first steps in August 2011 and is now racing around at home, leaving us blessed that we have another healthy boy to marvel over.

Photographs of Samuel Heagney.

Samuel after first operation

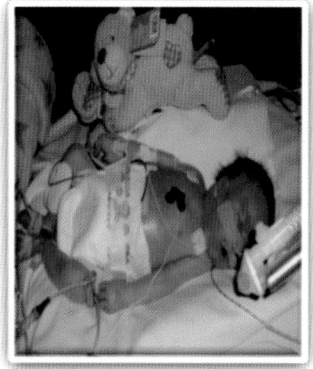

Samuel's first Christmas

Samuel's first birthday

Samuel and Mummy

œ

Sarah Rose O'Callaghan and Rebecca Rose O'Callaghan (rest in peace) (30 weeks) and Jonathon O'Callaghan (rest in peace) and Amy O'Callaghan (rest in peace) (22 weeks)

A couple of months after my husband Derek and I got married in 1990, we decided to start a new life in Nairobi, Kenya. We settled in there very well, and a few months later we were delighted to discover that I was expecting our first child. I had a very easy pregnancy, and the only thing that really worried me at the time was that there was no epidural facility at the hospital I was attending. At 40 weeks, I was out shopping and felt a bit strange. I went to my obstetrician later that day, and he informed me that I was having a painless labour and was in fact 5 cm dilated. I had no pain at all, and after a very short labour our son Andrew was born, weighing 2.78 kg (6 lb 2 oz).

When Andrew was two years old we decided it was time for him to have a brother or sister, but unfortunately it turned out that it was not going to be as easy to conceive our second child. We tried for nearly a year, and when I did eventually conceive, I had a miscarriage at 11 weeks. Our next pregnancy ended in an ectopic pregnancy and a life-saving operation as my fallopian tube had ruptured. We subsequently went on to have five more ectopic pregnancies, and in the end our doctors advised us that IVF was our only hope. Although this was a big shock, we went into the whole process with huge optimism and, I suppose in a way, naivety. Amazingly, we fell pregnant following our second IVF attempt, but very unexpectedly I went into premature labour at 22 weeks. Again it was a painless labour, and I had no idea that I was 5 cm dilated when I got to the hospital thinking I was just experiencing Braxton Hicks contractions. Jonathon and Amy were born a few hours later. They lived just one precious hour.

We were absolutely devastated, but after a few months we picked ourselves up and decided to try again. We were not so lucky this time, and every failed cycle was heartbreaking. It eventually took seven more IVF attempts to achieve another pregnancy, and this time I was expecting twins again: two girls. Sadly, at my ten-week scan we discovered that one of our precious girls had neural-tube defects which were not compatible with life. It was also not known if her twin would survive if she died *in utero*. I had a suture placed at 20 weeks as my cervix started to dilate and remained on bed rest, praying that my sick little girl would hang on for her sister. When we learnt that one of our girls would die soon after birth, we chose names for the girls: Sarah Rose and Rebecca Rose. I got to know Rebecca more each day and cherished every little kick, knowing that I would have very little time with her when she was born.

Sarah stopped growing at 26 weeks due to IUGR, and when my waters broke on 27 July, at 30 weeks, I gave birth to my beautiful little girls, both weighing less than 0.9 kg (2 lb). Sarah was taken to NICU, and Rebecca remained in our arms as we said goodbye to her. She was so beautiful. She knew we were there, but she was struggling to stay alive, so we kissed her and told her it was OK to go to Heaven.

Sarah spent two weeks in high dependency and was very tiny. Her whole hand was the size of her daddy's thumbnail. At three weeks she was moved to the NICU as she had acquired an infection and was very ill. Then her bilirubin levels started to rise, and she had to have five blood transfusions. She was then transferred to isolation as she was carrying MRSA. We were so scared. We had already buried three babies and just prayed day and night that she would survive.

Sarah finally came home after three months, weighing 1.81 kg (4 lb). She is now a feisty and clever little girl and has just completed two years of playschool. When we look at her we never stop counting our blessings and, of course, remembering our little angels, Rebecca and Jonathon and Amy. Sarah now has a one-year-old brother, Adam, who was also conceived through IVF. He also tried to make an early appearance at 20 weeks, but, with a suture inserted and bed rest, miraculously he was born at 38 weeks. Our family is now complete, and we feel very blessed and very lucky.

Photographs of Sarah Rose O'Callaghan.

Sarah, two weeks old

Sarah, one month old

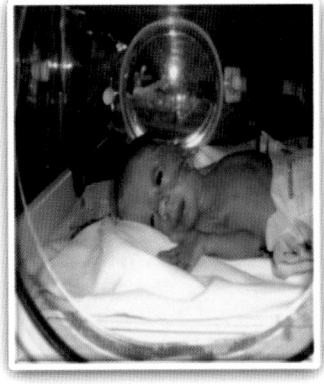

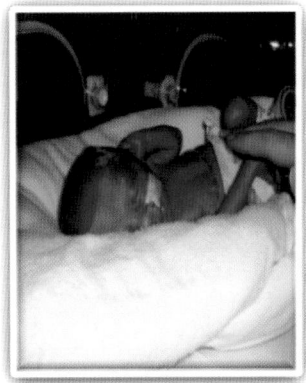

Sarah, three months old

Sarah today

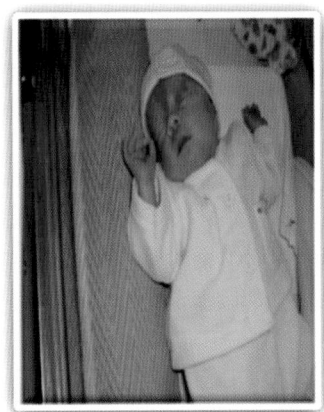

႙

Shannon Flaherty (31 weeks)

When we first decided to try for a baby I thought getting pregnant would be the hardest part. I thought once you got pregnant everything would be perfect after that. How wrong can you be? I was 31 weeks pregnant when things started to go wrong. A routine appointment in Sligo General Hospital showed that my blood pressure was up. I had protein in my urine, and my bump was measuring 28 weeks in size rather than the 31 weeks it should have been. I was given a blood-pressure monitor and sent home. At home I read up on pre-eclampsia but couldn't possibly believe this could be happening to me. Results from the monitor the next day indicated that all was fine, so I returned to work that afternoon. I had a scan the following day, and it showed that there was reduced fluid around the baby which meant they couldn't see the baby very well. I was kept in hospital for observation and given the steroid injections to help develop the baby's lungs.

The following day things didn't improve, and at one stage there was a fasting sign put up on my bed for surgery. I was told 'it would be best if you ring your husband to come'. The doctor and nurse explained to my husband and I how serious things were, and I was told that the neonatal transport team were going to transfer me to the NMH in Dublin. The staff in Sligo felt it would be in the baby's best interest to be sent to a bigger unit with more specialist equipment because they suspected the baby was going to be very small. By 11.00 p.m. that night I was in Dublin and thinking that this was going to be my home for the next couple of weeks. The following morning I had a lot of tests carried out. That evening the baby's heart rate was beginning to weaken so it was decided that I need an emergency section.

At 11.00 p.m. on 13 September our little baby girl Shannon Rose was born. She was a tiny 1.33 kg (2 lb 15 oz) and had a good set of lungs on her despite her size and gestation. We got to see her beautiful little face, with her big eyes wide open in amazement, for just a few moments before she was taken away to the NICU. When I went to see her there it was so surreal. When I had seen her in the operating theatre before they had taken her away she was wrapped in a blanket and didn't look as small as everyone had said she was going to be, but here in an incubator, with only a nappy on, she was tiny.

She should have been still inside me but here she was in a Dublin hospital in an incubator. She was all on her own and I couldn't protect her. How would she know I was her mammy? I felt the whole delivery and birth happened so quickly that I barely had any time to process what was happening. One of the hardest moments for me was when I was discharged and I had to leave her. It's so difficult to explain the sorrow and anguish you feel as a mother when you are separated from your baby, and there's not a thing you can do about it. Of course I put on a brave face but inside my heart was breaking.

Shannon spent a week in Dublin, and then she was transferred back to Sligo. She had strong lungs but as she was so small she needed time to grow and put on weight. She was a very poor feeder, and it would take for ever for her to drink tiny amounts of fluids then to throw it back up again. It was a constant worry for the first few months.

Shannon continued to slowly gain weight and to progress better with her feeding. After a four-week stay in Sligo, after five long weeks of separation, our little Shannon came home, and we finally got to show everyone our precious first child. Despite Shannon arriving eight weeks early she thankfully hasn't encountered any major health problems, and today she is happy and full of life. Shannon now has a little sister, who I am happy to say was full term, and what a lucky girl she is to have a big sister like Shannon.

Photographs of Shannon Flaherty.

Shannon, three days old

Shannon, five months old

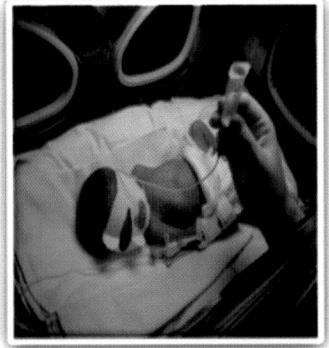

Shannon, one and a half

Shannon, two years, five months

CR

Teagan Weldon (32 weeks)

My waters broke whilst alone at home, at 30 weeks pregnant. Having contacted the Rotunda in Dublin I was advised to go to hospital immediately. I was to be admitted for observation as my waters had half broken. I was in shock and terrified that the baby was arriving early. Would she be OK? Why was this happening? My mind raced with questions for which I didn't have answers.

At 12 midnight on day 3 of my hospital admission I felt what I thought might be a contraction. After 20 minutes the pain intensified. I was rushed to the delivery ward, and, without pain relief, Teagan was born at 1.03 a.m. on 14 May, weighing 1.76 kg (3 lb 14 oz). She was born one hour after the first contraction. Teagan was rushed to the NICU, and, after an hour, the nursing staff brought me to see her there. All I could see were tubes and bandages; I couldn't see my tiny baby. The shock of the experience left me unable to cry. I just wanted to hold my little baby but couldn't.

The following days I functioned on autopilot. Thankfully I was able to spend every day at Teagan's incubator as I live near the hospital. Each day brought the heart-wrenching ache of leaving the hospital without my baby and going home to a house full of baby stuff. Every day I saw parents bringing their babies home and I felt cheated as my baby should have been home with me too. Every night I left, not knowing if I would get a call from the medical staff advising me that Teagan's condition had worsened or if I'd see her again the next day. Comments such as 'Well at least you can get some sleep' were, to say the least, unhelpful and hurtful, and I would often just want to scream back, 'How would you sleep if your baby was gravely ill in intensive care and you were unable to stay with them at night?'

I had to live one day at a time, praying, hoping every day that Teagan would gain in strength. After one month in the NICU and weighing 2.27 kg (5 lb), Teagan was finally well enough to go home. She was still very tiny, so small that she fitted in my hand. I was so excited to get her home and to introduce her to my friends and family. Gradually the initial excitement turned to fear. I was at home on my own with a premature baby. It was really difficult; she was so small that even changing her nappy or clothes was a task in itself. I was so nervous. She vomited after every bottle and screamed most of the time. I was drained physically and emotionally and was later diagnosed with PND, a fact attributed by my doctor to the experience of Teagan's early arrival and uncertain prognosis. My wonderful friends and family rallied around and helped us to get through the next couple of months. They looked after the baby and me. I will always be grateful to them.

Teagan had a few problems. She wasn't gaining weight and was put on prescribed formula as she was classed as 'failure to thrive'. She was also born with a cleft palate, for which she had an operation at nine months, and her immature immune system resulted in her being unwell frequently. At the time of her cleft-palate surgery she was diagnosed with PRS, a rare syndrome associated with cleft palate. She has a small chin, jaw and mouth, which can cause breathing problems, and she is under the care of a specialist team at Temple Street Children's University Hospital in Dublin. She has speech therapy and will need regular hearing tests as these are complications associated with cleft palate and PRS.

Teagan's development is behind other term babies her age, but she is doing great. She is a happy, beautiful baby who loves playing and chatting away. She will most likely continue to have problems with her health, but after all she has been through so far I know she will be just fine. Having a premature baby is not easy, especially if you're on your own, but you learn to cope. It is so important to accept people's help and, most of all, to realise that your premature baby is the greatest gift you will ever receive.

Photographs of Teagan Weldon.

Teagan, 12 hours old

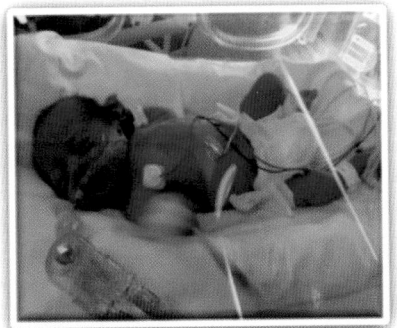

Teagan's home-coming party

Teagan, starting to sit up by herself, St Patrick's Day

Teagan, one year old

Thomas Kinlan Lawlor (31 weeks)

Thomas was born on 4 July in the Rotunda Hospital, Dublin. He was born at 31 weeks, weighing 1.36 kg (3 lb), and he went straight to the NICU. After 24 hours, Thomas came off the ventilator and was able to breathe for himself, and I was able to hold him for the first time. On 9 July, Thomas was moved to the SCBU because he was doing very well, but during that night he became ill and was put back on a ventilator. We were then informed that he had NEC. A few hours later, Thomas's bowel perforated, and he had to be transferred to Temple Street Children's University Hospital's ICU where surgeons were waiting to look at his scans and to operate.

When the surgeons looked at the scans and examined Thomas, they called me and Thomas's dad into a room and told us that Thomas was too ill for surgery. The next 72 hours were critical. They decided to put a tube into his bowel to drain out as much of the infection as they could and to start him on three strong antibiotics. Thomas spent three weeks in ICU. For days we were told there was no improvement, and by then his lung had collapsed from being on the ventilator. It was heartbreaking to see our child go through this.

At last we got a bit of good news: Thomas was showing signs of improvement and could have surgery. He had part of his bowel removed and was left with a stoma bag for six months. A few days after surgery, he was moved down to the HDU. Thomas was doing well, but his output in the stoma bag was too high, and he was not gaining enough weight. Three weeks later, Thomas was taken out of the incubator and moved to a cot. He was then moved to a ward, but he was still having problems with his output, even though he was on TPN from the time he got sick.

The doctors needed to know why Thomas's output was too high, so in October he was transferred to Our Lady's Children's Hospital in Crumlin to see the gastroenterology specialist. They decided to keep Thomas on TPN and to keep him in Crumlin. In December, the gastroenterology team decided that Thomas needed to have his stoma reversed, which might stop the high output and help him gain weight on his own, so he was transferred back to Temple Street Children's University Hospital for surgery. This was arranged for 5 January 2011, and Thomas was allowed home for the first time ever on 13 December 2010, and he got to spend Christmas at home.

On 4 January 2011, I brought Thomas back to Temple Street to prepare for surgery the following morning at 8.00 a.m., but at 5.00 a.m. Thomas's bowel prolapsed, and he had to go for surgery straight away. I had to give permission for surgery on the phone in case I didn't get to the hospital in time. I went straight to the hospital and was told they were unsure if he would have the reversal after all. When Thomas came back from surgery the reversal had been done, but the surgeon had had to remove more of his bowel. He went back to ICU for two days before being moved to a ward. Thomas was still having problems with his output so he was transferred back to Crumlin in the middle of January, where he went to theatre to have a broviac line inserted for administration of TPN.

Thomas suffers with short gut syndrome as a result of NEC. He was released on 27 May 2011 and still attends Crumlin on a weekly basis to monitor his weight and to have his broviac line flushed. The broviac line remains in situ in the event that TPN needs to be administered. Thomas is on a special diet and a lot of medication, but apart from that he is doing very well.

Photographs of Thomas Lee Kinlan Lawlor.

Thomas, a few hours old

Thomas, seven months old receiving TPN

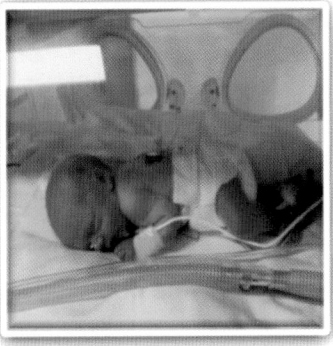

Thomas, nine months old, first spoon-feed

Thomas, 11 months old, first week home

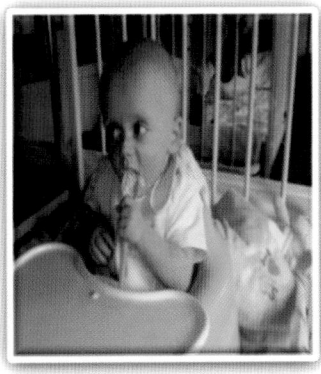

Your Baby's Diary

Mother's name:

Father's name:

Baby's name:

Date of birth:

Time of birth:

Weight at birth:

Length at birth:

Hospital of birth:

Gestation:

Due date:

A special doctor or nurse to us and our baby:

Memories of the Birth

Those First Special Times

First time we saw you:

First time we touched you:

First time you opened your eyes:

First time we changed your nappy:

First time you wrapped your finger around ours:

First cuddle with Mam:

First cuddle with Dad:

First time we heard you cry:

First time you breathed on your own:

First time we did skin-to-skin care:

First time you took a feed:

First time you wore some clothing:

First time family got to meet you:

First time you went into a cot:

First time you had a bath: